RATIONING MEDICINE

Threats from European Cost-Effectiveness
Models to America's Seniors and other
Vulnerable Populations

WRITTEN BY
William Smith, PhD

PIONEER INSTITUTE
PUBLIC POLICY RESEARCH

PIONEER INSTITUTE
PUBLIC POLICY RESEARCH

Pioneer's **mission** is to develop and communicate dynamic ideas that advance prosperity and a vibrant civic life in Massachusetts and beyond.

Pioneer's **vision of success** is a state and nation where our people can prosper and our society thrive because we enjoy world-class options in education, health care, transportation, and economic opportunity, and where our government is limited, accountable, and transparent.

Pioneer **values** an America where our citizenry is well-educated and willing to test our beliefs based on facts and the free exchange of ideas, and committed to liberty, personal responsibility, and free enterprise.

CONTENTS

CHAPTER 1

Introduction

The costs of prescription drugs are a prominent issue for state and federal legislators across the nation. Research and development trends in the pharmaceutical industry are yielding more and more therapies for rare and orphan diseases, therapies that typically have much higher prices than traditional small-molecule drugs. While the economics of drugs for rare diseases are well established, i.e. drugs that target a smaller pool of patients with very serious diseases tend to be much more expensive, some policy makers have expressed sticker shock at the prices of certain therapies and are exploring options to try and lower them.

The Emergence of QALY

One strategy that policy makers are considering is the adoption of so-called cost-effectiveness reviews that purport to be objective methods of evaluating whether particular therapies are overpriced. The National Institute for Health and Care Excellence (NICE) in the United Kingdom (UK) developed the most prominent methodology for cost-effectiveness reviews beginning in the 1970s. NICE's methodology uses the "Quality Adjusted Life Year" (QALY) standard, which assigns a monetary value to the quality of life and survival-length for patients and then assesses the cost-effectiveness of a drug based upon the drug's potential to both improve a patient's quality of life and extend that life.

While a number of aspects of the NICE model have generated controversy, many criticisms flow from the use of the QALY standard. One QALY equals one full year of life in perfect health.

The value of one QALY is assigned a monetary value. In the United States, the Institute of Clinical and Economic Review (ICER), a nonprofit begun in 2006 out of Harvard Medical School as a program that did cost-effectiveness analyses of health care generally, but which began focusing on drug prices in 2014, has, like NICE, adopted the QALY standard. ICER values one year of perfect health at about $100,000–$150,000.

QALY therefore includes in a single cost index the combined value of the length and quality of life. When patients need a certain therapy, the QALY model assigns a value to the therapy based on how long it would prolong the patient's life and how much it would raise the quality of that prolonged life.

Despite its adoption by such nations as the UK, Canada and Australia, the use of QALY has generated controversy elsewhere. The United States and Germany have both rejected the standard's use, and one major health outcomes study of the 27 European health systems conducted by the *European Consortium in Healthcare Outcomes and cost benefit research* concluded that, "QALY assessment for health decision making should be abandoned."

Even in the UK, NICE's methodology has generated significant criticism from both patient advocates and physicians, as well as from the biopharmaceutical industry. There is some evidence that NICE's reviews have made the latest pharmacopeia less available to British patients than to patients in other nations. This is for two reasons. First, therapies are typically denied to patients in the National Health Service until a NICE review has certified that these new drugs are cost-effective, and then, once NICE has completed its review, many therapies are deemed not cost-effective, and thus are permanently denied to patients, at least until a subsequent review.

Some of the most intense criticism of NICE's methodology has come from oncology, where critics have noted that delays in NICE reviews were, quite literally, causing the deaths of patients who were awaiting reviews of new cancer treatments already widely available in other countries. To circumvent the NICE review process, in April of 2010, then-Prime Minister David Cameron announced the creation of a Cancer Drugs Fund that would fund cancer treatments regardless of the conclusions of a NICE cost-effectiveness review. In announcing the Cancer Drugs Fund, Cameron said: "Other European countries are doing better than us at giving people longer, happier lives with cancer. We want to get more drugs to people more quickly and in the UK today there are some people — thousands of people — who want a certain cancer drug, whose doctors tell them they should have a certain cancer drug, who don't get it."

The creation of the Cancer Drugs Fund highlights some of the most serious issues surrounding the use of the QALY standard in assessing the value of therapies for dreaded diseases. It seems clear that the people of the United Kingdom, and their elected officials, were not comfortable with the monetary value assigned to human life by the QALY standard, as it resulted in the denial of life-saving drugs.

ICER and the United States

In the United States, ICER has adopted a cost-effectiveness methodology similar to NICE that also uses the QALY standard. Despite the intense criticism in the UK that this methodology has led to drug rationing, some US policy makers are considering using ICER's conclusions for structuring government drug formularies. For example, the New York State Medicaid program used an ICER review to evaluate whether to pay for ORKAMBI, a breakthrough treatment for cystic fibrosis.

The pharmacy benefit management company CVS Caremark also recently announced that it would begin using ICER data for its formulary management and would establish a hard QALY threshold of $100,000; i.e., if a drug could not prove a value above $100,000, it would not be covered. CVS's use of ICER data is particularly controversial because, if the company were to succeed at lowering a drug's price based on an ICER review, the reduction in price would likely take the form of a higher rebate payment from the drug manufacturer that would flow to CVS itself, not necessarily a reduction in the patient's out-of-pocket cost. Rebate payments do not flow to patients, they are the result of contracts between pharmacy benefit managers, such as CVS Caremark, and drug manufacturers.

There have long been rumors that the Veterans Administration (VA) has used QALY reviews to construct the VA formulary. This would be troubling as it would likely indicate a lower quality of care for Americans veterans.

However, a more troubling expansion of the use of the QALY would be in the Medicare program, the healthcare program for America's seniors. Fortunately, the Biden Administration has thrown cold water on the potential use of the QALY in a report issued by U.S. Health Secretary Becerra on September 9, 2021.

Nonetheless, federal policy makers should monitor the quality of Medicare formularies carefully. The Centers for Medicare and Medicaid (CMS) recently announced that Medicare Part D plans could begin adopting indication-based criteria for their drug formularies in 2020.

Currently, once a drug is approved on a Part D formulary, it can be prescribed for all FDA-approved indications, while an indication-based formulary may cover the drug for one disease state but not another. Some health policy experts have concluded that CMS's adoption of indication-based formularies portends the adoption of cost-effectiveness studies, such as the use of ICER reviews, when assembling drug formularies for older Americans and the disabled.

ICER and American Political Culture

U.S. policy makers have a genuine budgetary challenge in addressing high-cost treatments for patients with serious diseases. Some form of cost-effectiveness measures are needed by private and government payers as judgements need to be made which keep payers solvent. However, the QALY model offers significant infirmities that harm patients. ICER cost-effectiveness reviews seem particularly controversial for older patients, those with disabilities, cancer patients, and patients with rare diseases. Given these controversies, policy makers may want to tread carefully. It seems unlikely that the American public will accept the kinds of rationing of therapies and medical services that the British public, after 70 years of socialized medicine, has largely come to accept. The political firestorm in the US would likely be far greater than it was in the UK if U.S. senior citizens were temporarily denied new oncology treatments while the federal government conducted cost-effectiveness reviews, and would probably be even more pointed if that review were to conclude that U.S. seniors should be denied a new oncology treatment that was available to citizens in other countries.

A similar political backlash may occur in state Medicaid programs that serve as a safety net for many of the very patients suffering from rare and debilitating diseases. A large number of patients in Medicaid and in the prison system do not currently have access to many of the latest treatments. Would advocates for the poor permit even more tightly restricting access to medications for these populations if ICER reviews made such recommendations? Again, the American public may be less accepting than the British public if a disabled child in the Medicaid program were denied a lifesaving or life altering therapy because of an ICER review.

For the New England area, and the Boston-Cambridge area in particular, the adoption of cost-effectiveness methodologies also could have consequences for economic development, as the region contains a large cluster of biopharmaceutical companies that are the very entities discovering new therapies for rare disease. If the adoption of ICER-style reviews were to become widespread, it would likely have a harmful economic impact, as these reviews would target the very therapies being developed by New England's biopharmaceutical companies.

The impact could well be significant, as widespread adoption of ICER's model in the US is quite likely to accelerate some existing adverse trends in the biopharma industry. At the very least, depending upon some of their conclusions, ICER reviews, if adopted, are likely to steer companies away from research into certain therapeutic areas that ICER deems less cost-effective. Therefore, certain groups of patients would likely see less innovation toward cures for their particular diseases.

To inform this debate, Pioneer Institute conducted research during 2019 on ICER's methodology and its potential impact, most importantly the impact upon certain vulnerable groups of patients, but also upon the New England regional economy. As part of that work, Pioneer prepared a list of questions policy makers should ask when considering the adoption of ICER-style cost-effectiveness reviews. The questions are not designed to offer definitive conclusions about ICER, but they represent a summary of the questions and concerns raised in academic literature about the limitations of ICER's model.

I present these questions at the end of the book, hopeful that they may illuminate some of the potential impacts of ICER's model on patients, physicians, and drug discovery and, in this way, help policy makers reach the most thoughtful conclusions about use of ICER's methodology. But, though the impacts on all three need to be considered when making any decisions about the use of ICER, I have chosen here, in this volume, to focus my attention on patients, for it will be they who bear the hardest brunt and they whom policy makers should keep uppermost in mind.

I begin with the elderly.

CHAPTER 2

Quality Adjusted Life Year (QALY): The Threat to Older Americans

The Quality-Adjusted Life Year (QALY) cost-effectiveness methodology employed most notably in the U.S. by the Institute for Clinical and Economic Review (ICER) and in the United Kingdom by The National Institute for Health and Care Excellence (NICE) represents an inherently discriminatory threat to senior citizens' access to high-quality medicines. The threat that QALY poses to older Americans deserves considerable attention because some observers argue that, were the U.S. to implement a "Medicare for All" health plan, cost pressures would inevitably lead federal policy makers to adopt the use of QALYs when making decisions on how to ration healthcare[1].

More importantly, in the wake of the coronavirus pandemic, when the nation's older adults were, and remain, at higher risk of getting very sick from the COVID-19 virus,[2] it would seem a highly suspect public health policy for the nation to adopt QALY, a cost-effectiveness methodology that has the potential to deny seniors access to life-saving treatments.

While there is considerable academic literature pointing to the problematic aspects of utilizing QALYs to make decisions about access to medicines for senior populations, one need not employ a sophisticated economic model to understand the nature of the issue. (A good summary of the academic literature around the limitations of QALYs can be found in "The Limitations of QALY: A Literature Review," *Journal of Stem Cell Research & Therapy* 2016.)

QALYs rate medicines according to their ability to extend life and to improve the quality of life. As one researcher described it in the *Journal of Medical Ethics*: "The QALY combines life expectancy after treatment with measures of the expected quality of life." Because older adults would, by definition, exhibit shorter life expectancy, medicines used by senior citizens would expect a lower QALY score.

The same researcher goes on to point out: "(I)n every case QALYs are indeed inherently ageist and also favour those with greater life expectancy regardless of age. This must be the case because length of lifetime to be gained, is both valued and built into the way QALYs are calculated."[3] Treatments that provide more "life years" will be rated as "more effective" under QALY, which superficially sounds commonsensical unless you realize that this standard will, by definition, be used to argue that drugs for senior citizens with shorter life expectancies will be rated lower than drugs for younger people.

Another academic researcher of QALYs reached the same conclusion: "(E)lderly patients, who by having a shorter lifespan, may forgo any improvements in QALYs that accrue over subsequent decades. Such improvements would therefore only be seen to benefit younger (and potentially healthier) individuals."[4]

Some have argued that NICE and ICER have taken steps to mitigate the discriminatory effects of QALYs on older adults. A decade ago, NICE endured significant criticism for the use of "ageist" methodology. Critics argued that NICE's decisions were a violation of the UK's Equality Act of 2010 that bans age discrimination. In response, NICE launched a noteworthy review of its processes to ensure that its decisions were not discriminatory.

In arguing that the National Health Service now more thoroughly considers the views of patients, one set of British researchers argued that the National Health Service now uses "citizen councils" and "advisory committees" to enforce "social value principles" that protect against "ageist" decisions. They also pointed to anecdotal evidence of decisions that favored certain treatments for older adults. They finally concluded that "NICE has implemented robust systems to identify potential for discrimination and developed clear mechanisms to avoid and resolve it."[5]

Likewise, in the U.S., ICER has been criticized by some senior citizen advocacy groups for its use of QALYs. In response, ICER continued to defend its use of QALY but announced in 2018 that it would simultaneously adopt another measure of clinical benefit, the so-called "Equal Value of Life Years Gained" (evLYG), a methodology that ICER argues "evenly measures any gains in length of life, regardless of the treatment's ability to improve patients' quality of life." However, ICER insisted that the use of the evLYG will be "supplementing the QALY, not replacing it."[6]

At any rate, researchers at Tufts Medical Center have pointed out that the evLYG methodology, even if used exclusively and not in concert with QALYs, can produce very problematic and discriminatory results. "The evLYG measure has its own discriminatory implications, however…and…cost-per-QALY and cost-per-evLYG assessments usually produce results that differ modestly."[7]

These defenses of NICE's and ICER's use of QALYs to rate treatments for seniors are remarkably unpersuasive. One can establish citizen councils or use other methodologies to supplement QALY, but the reality is that the QALY methodology values life extension when rating the cost-effectiveness of medicine. Older adults have fewer QALYs to give, so the formula will always contain an inherent bias against medicine for older adults, with greatest discrimination against the frailest and most elderly.

QALYs and the Rationing of Care for the Elderly

The problematic aspects of QALYs for the elderly become quite clear with a simple example. Imagine that a 25-year-old man and a 70-year-old man live with the same disease. A cure becomes available at a cost of $200,000 that will restore both individuals to a full quality of life and a life expectancy of 80 years of age. Under the QALY methodology, the younger person will gain 55 life-years while the older person will gain only 10. The medicine will be rated as much more cost-effective for the 25-year-old man because of the QALYs gained. When bureaucracies in nationalized healthcare systems make decisions about how to ration various treatments using QALYs, it will be judged much more cost-effective to treat younger people with this $200,000 medicine than to treat older patients. This is exactly how rationing decisions are currently justified in many non-U.S. healthcare systems.

Many medical "ethicists" support the rationing of care for the elderly and say so openly. In 1987, Daniel Callahan, a medical "ethicist" at the Hastings Center in New York, famously wrote a book titled: "Setting Limits: Medical Goals in an Aging Society," which "faults our health care system for devoting disproportionate resources and technology on extending the lives of the elderly regardless of the quality of their lives." In 2009, when Callahan was 79, he suffered a cardiac event and quickly underwent an $80,000 treatment, a decision that drew some criticism given his past positions.[8] Given his advanced age, a decision to deny this $80,000 treatment might be justified by the use of QALY methodology, as Callahan may not have secured enough "life years" to make the treatment cost-effective.

The Problem of Palliative Care

The infirmities of QALY are clearly demonstrated in the bias of the methodology against palliative care. A just and compassionate society will always seek to treat older, terminally ill patients with dignity during their final days. This means taking steps to make them feel comfortable and providing them with treatments that may lessen their pain and anxiety. Yet, QALY, because of the way it works, has an inherent bias against providing these types of treatments.

As discussed, QALY cost-effectiveness scores are based on

the ability of a treatment to extend life and to improve the quality of life. While palliative care treatments might significantly improve the quality of a patient's life in their final days, they often do not extend it. As one researcher has pointed out, "palliative care interventions will produce positive QALY scores to the extent that they improve patients' quality of life."

The problem, however, is that although successful palliative care interventions produce benefits that can be measured in QALYs, they do not achieve high QALY scores. Because palliative care deals with the terminally ill, the improvements in the quality of life that it achieves for its patients is inevitably short-lived. Thus, even when palliative care effects very substantial improvement in its patients' quality of life, the additional number of QALYs generated is small in comparison with treatments that save patients from premature death, or which produce similar improvements in quality of life for patients with longer life expectancy. This is what we refer to as palliative care's 'QALY problem.'"[9]

Palliative care highlights the problem of using the QALY methodology generally: not every decision made in healthcare should be justified solely based on cost-effectiveness. Human beings make value judgments about how to care for their fellow human beings. These decisions can become morally grotesque when decisions are made exclusively by healthcare economists using cost-effectiveness formulas. These formulas themselves are based upon certain value judgments that human life is less valuable than many Americans think.

A New Way to Think About the Economic Value of Older Adults

If we think of older adults in economic terms, what the economists at NICE and ICER ignore is the tremendous economic value that longer lives have brought to society. The methodologies that NICE and ICER use see senior citizens as an economic problem, but they should instead see them as an economic engine.

In 2006, two University of Chicago economists pointed out that, during the 20th century, the life expectancy of Americans increased by about 30 years. The result has not been a "problem for the healthcare system" but a cascade of wealth creation. "Cumulative gains in life expectancy after 1900 were worth over $1.2 million to the representative American in 2000, whereas post-1970 gains added about $3.2 trillion per year to national wealth, equal to about half of GDP...For men, mortality reductions between 1970 and 1980 were worth $27 *trillion*."[10]

These economists' conclusions are precisely the opposite of what rings in our ears every day about the "unsustainable" costs of healthcare. "Even ignoring health-induced changes in quality of life, we find that the aggregate value of increased longevity since 1970 has greatly exceeded additional costs of health care."

Rather than finding ways to deny treatments that may extend the life of an older patient, these economists argued that we should be making larger and larger investments in research that might extend the life of older patients. "(T)ake our estimate that a 1 percent reduction in cancer mortality would be worth about $500 billion. Then, a "war on cancer" that would spend an additional $100 billion on cancer research and treatment would be worthwhile if it has a one in five chance of reducing mortality by 1 percent and a four in five chance of doing nothing at all."

Conclusion

During the 2020 Democratic presidential primaries, proposals to create a "Medicare for All" healthcare system came to the fore. Candidates argued that such a nationalized healthcare system would save a great deal of money because the government could impose lower prices and avoid duplicative paperwork, thus containing the growth in healthcare costs.

But ICER continues to insist that QALYs represent the best way to control healthcare costs. As it said recently: "The Institute for Clinical and Economic Review (ICER) has posted a summary of the reasons that the quality-adjusted life year (QALY) is the gold standard for measuring how well a medical treatment improves patients' lives."[11]

Senior citizens who become enrolled in a Medicare for All plan and are then denied valuable treatments based upon a QALY cost-effectiveness review might not share ICER's view on the value of QALYs. Not only is ICER's modeling of the value of longevity flawed, it also devalues treatments such as palliative care that are extremely important to older Americans and their families, but which may not increase longevity.

Finally, because senior citizens have been, and continue to be, particularly vulnerable during the COVID-19 pandemic, America's health plans should be doing precisely the opposite of what ICER tends to recommend: they should make medicines for seniors and vulnerable populations widely and easily available. Copays and coinsurance should be reduced significantly or eliminated. Formularies should be loosened for these populations so treatments for underlying conditions are readily and easily available to the vulnerable.

The nation has spent trillions of dollars combatting the pandemic and its economic impact. Why do that only to turn around and begin denying elderly patients, among the populations who most benefited from the government's investment in vaccines, access to potentially life-saving and life-extending drugs for other ailments? One simple reform that will help protect older Americans from COVID-19 will be to give them quick and ready access to treatments their doctors want them to have. We want those who may be exposed to the virus to be in the best possible health when they are.

Having looked at the potential impact of using QALYs on the elderly, we now turn our attention to another vulnerable population, the medically disabled, whose access to innovative new treatments for the ailments from which they suffer may be restricted by the use of QALYs, which could represent a violation of the American Disabilities Act.

CHAPTER 3

The Legality of QALY under the ADA

Does a state government violate the Americans with Disabilities Act (ADA) when it uses "quality of life" standards as a factor in determining which medical treatments are available to patients through their Medicaid programs?

If used to rate the cost-effectiveness of medical treatments available to Medicaid patients, the QALY methodology would be extremely vulnerable to challenge under the Americans with Disabilities Act.[12]

That said, the use of QALYs by state governments to administer Medicaid to disabled persons would be extremely vulnerable to challenge under the ADA if the priority were the achievement of "asymptomatic" status, rather than "medical effectiveness," resulting in the provision of lesser benefits. This outcome, which would have a disparate impact on individuals with both physical and mental disabilities, would be a clear violation of the ADA.

Definitions

The term "qualified individual with a disability" means "an individual with a disability who, with or without reasonable modifications to rules, policies, or practices, the removal of architectural, communication, or transportation barriers, or the provision of auxiliary aids and services, meets the essential eligibility requirements for the receipt of services or the participation in programs or activities provided by a public entity."[13]

THE TERM "PUBLIC ENTITY" MEANS: "(a) any State or local government; (b) any department, agency, special purpose district or other instrumentality of a State or local government; and (c) the National Railroad Passenger Corporation, and any commuter authority as defined in Title 49 of the United States Code." 42 U.S.C. § 12131(1)

Background

Enacted in 1965 as Title XIX of the Social Security Act, the Medicaid Act is a cooperative federal-state program designed to provide medical assistance to persons whose resources are insufficient to meet the costs of their necessary medical care.[14] Although a state is not required to participate in the Medicaid program, once it chooses to do so it must develop a plan that complies with the Medicaid statute and the regulations promulgated by the Secretary of the Department of Health and Human Services (USHHS).[15] State Medicaid plans must also comply with other federal law, such as the ADA and the United States Constitution.

The ADA was passed by the Federal Government in 1990 and addresses broad discrimination against persons with disabilities. In the introductory provision of the ADA, Congress shared its findings applicable to all forms of discrimination that the ADA was meant to prohibit. Findings most relevant to our current analysis are the following:

"(1) physical or mental disabilities in no way diminish a person's right to fully participate in all aspects of society, yet many people with physical or mental disabilities have been precluded from doing so because of discrimination; others who have a record of a disability or are regarded as having a disability also have been subjected to discrimination;"

"(2) historically, society has tended to isolate and segregate individuals with disabilities, and, despite some improvements, such forms of discrimination against individuals with disabilities continue to be a serious and pervasive social problem;"

"(3) discrimination against individuals with disabilities persists in such critical areas as…institutionalization, health services…and access to public services;"…

"(5) individuals with disabilities continually encounter various forms of discrimination, including outright intentional exclusion…exclusionary qualification standards and criteria, segregation, and relegation to lesser services, programs, activities, benefits, jobs, or other opportunities."[16]

The ADA prohibits discrimination in employment practices (Title I, §§ 12111–12117), public services furnished by "public entities" (Title II, §§ 12131–12165), and public accommodations provided by private entities (Title III, §§ 12181–12189). The Rehabilitation Act provided the foundation for the ADA, and courts, when interpreting the ADA, frequently find support in cases brought under the Rehabilitation Act. *DuBois v. Alderson-Broaddus College, Inc.*, 950 F. Supp. 754, 760 (N.D.W. Va. 1997).

With healthcare spending steadily rising each year in the United States, there is a need for methods that identify treatments with the highest value. Theoretically, covering high-value treatments, and dispensing with those with low value, will lower overall healthcare spending. As noted, one such method is the QALY, which attempts to assign relative value to a vast array of medical treatments using a single metric: quality of life.

There has been no shortage of criticism, however, over the potential of QALYs to discriminate against the disabled. Most notably, in the late 1980s and early 1990s the state of Oregon attempted to provide universal basic healthcare coverage to its low-income citizens. To do so, cost-saving techniques were proposed to ration the limited Medicaid funds available, including the prioritization of medical treatments based on ability to return a patient to an asymptomatic state. While the

QALY methodology is allegedly facially neutral, its measure of an individual's restoration to a certain quality of life is inherently discriminatory when applied to persons with physical or mental disabilities, who may seek treatment but never experience a quality of life recognized by this narrow methodology.

The first Bush Administration explicitly rejected the Oregon plan, based on concerns that the plan's use of QALY to measure allocation of Medicaid funds was discriminatory and in violation of the ADA. In July 1992, 20 disability advocacy organizations publicly urged President Bush to reject the waiver request required to enforce the Oregon plan. On August 3, 1992, then-HHS Secretary Louis Sullivan informed Oregon Governor Barbara Roberts that he would not grant the waiver, and argued that the survey informing research for the plan was "based in substantial part on the premise that the value of life of a person with a disability is less than the value of life of a person without a disability."

On January 19, 1993, the day before President Clinton's inauguration, a Bush Administration official in the Justice Department wrote to HHS that the revised plan continued to have "features that violate ADA," as priority was accorded to treatments that would "return the patient to an asymptomatic state of health" after saving his or her life. The letter argued that the designation "asymptomatic" denigrated the quality of life of persons with disabilities.

Despite intense opposition by more than 70 advocacy groups acquainted with the Americans with Disabilities Act, the Clinton Administration subsequently approved the "Oregon Reform Demonstration," and the plan was put into operation after all 29 terms and conditions required by the Department of Health and Human Services were satisfied. Included among these conditions was assurance that qualified disabled persons would not be denied accommodating care and treatments. Although declared a success, it is unclear whether Oregon's rationing plan has actually produced any savings at all.

Analysis

A. Title II Governs Public Programs Furnished by State Governments

The application of QALY to patients in public programs such as Medicaid is governed by Title II of the ADA as public services furnished by a "public entity."[17] Title II provides that:

> "Subject to the provisions of this subchapter, no qualified individual with a disability shall, by reason of such disability, be excluded from participation in or be denied the benefits of the services, programs, or activities of a public entity, or be subjected to discrimination by any such entity."[18]

Three factors must be shown to establish discrimination through services or programs furnished by a public entity under the ADA. First, the individual must show that they are a qualified individual with a disability. Second, the qualified individual must show that they were excluded from participation in a public entity's services, programs or activities or were otherwise discriminated against by a public entity. Third, such exclusion or discrimination must be shown to be due to their disability.[19]

Whether an individual is a qualified disabled person may only be determined on a case-by-case basis, but would be easily proven assuming a qualified individual brings a lawsuit. As for the second factor, a state government is a "public entity" and Medicaid is a "service" or "pro- gram."[20]

With these items established, QALY's legality under the ADA is left to one question: does QALY treat qualified disabled persons differently because of their disability?

B. The QALY Methodology Likely Violates the ADA When Applied to Medicaid Patients with Disabilities

The use of broad population-based cost and cost-effectiveness analyses in coverage decisions, without also using patient-specific metrics, is damaging and discriminatory against individuals with disabilities. People with disabilities and patients with chronic conditions often seek access to treatments and health interventions that improve their quality of life, even in the absence of a cure. Further, many people with disabilities may enjoy a quality of life comparable to non-disabled individuals, but may face a shorter life expectancy compared to someone without their condition. QALYs are determined by both quality as well as quantity of life, and thus, providing treatment to a non-disabled person with a longer life expectancy would be prioritized over a person with a disability or a life-shortening chronic condition.

QALY has the potential to unlawfully discriminate against disabled or chronically ill persons who may never experience full restoration to a certain quality of life defined by QALY. That treatments for disabilities may significantly improve one's quality of life, but never restore them to a "perfect" quality, renders such treatments subject to lower QALY values. Consequently, the QALY methodology may cause Medicaid programs to have a disparate impact, or discriminatory effect, on disabled persons, stemming from QALY assigning lower values to treatments for disabilities, thus rendering them less accessible to those whom they benefit.

C. QALY Could Readily Have a Disparate Impact on Treatments Available to Disabled Persons

Violations of the ADA may be founded on three theories of liability: (1) disparate treatment; (2) failure to make a reasonable accommodation; or (3) disparate impact. *Goord*, 591 F.3d at 43. So long as a QALY analysis does not explicitly evaluate treatments differently based on abilities or disabilities, a disparate treatment claim cannot succeed. Furthermore, an alleged failure to make a reasonable accommodation is extremely fact-specific, based on the circumstances surrounding the plaintiff's alleged discrimination. Therefore, determining whether a measure taken by a public entity was a reasonable accommodation of a disabled person's needs may only be made on a case-by-case basis.[21]

Disparate impact could, however, manifest in numerous forms when applying QALY to patients under Medicaid, because disparate impact is measured differently than disparate treatment. A facially neutral program, benefit, or service provided by a public entity creates a disparate impact when it has an actual or predictable discriminatory effect.[22]

QALY's preference for treatments that restore patients to 100 percent quality of life will disparately impact patients with disabilities, who will find treatments they may value, but which do not meet the 100 percent quality-of-life threshold, rated lower than treatments for non-disabled patients.

D. The Mental Health Parity and Addiction Equity Act ("MHPAEA") Requires Equal Treatment of Physical and Mental Disabilities

On September 5, 2019, the Departments of Labor (DOL), Health and Human Services (HHS), and the Treasury jointly issued the final rule on the Mental Health Parity and Addiction Equity Act ("MHPAEA"). The MHPAEA states that financial requirements, including coinsurance and copays, and treatment restrictions, such as visit limits, imposed on mental health or substance use disorder ("MH/SUD") benefits cannot be more restrictive than measures applied to substantially similar medical or surgical benefits. The MHPAEA narrows the permissible insurance coverage gap between treatments afforded to individuals with physical disabilities and those with mental disabilities. These requirements are applied across six classifications of benefits: (1) inpatient, in-network; (2) inpatient, out-of-network; (3) outpatient, in-network; (4) outpatient, out-of-network; (5) emergency care; and (6) prescription drugs.

Further, MHPAEA rules also apply to non-quantitative treatment limitations ("NQTL"), which are non-numerical limits on the scope or duration of benefits for treatment. As per the MHPAEA, a plan or issuer may not impose an NQTL on MH/SUD benefits unless all factors used in applying the NQTL are comparable to those used in assessing medical or surgical benefits. Federal MHPAEA regulations contain a non-exhaustive list of NQTLs that include: medical management standards limiting or excluding benefits based on medical necessity or medical appropriateness, or based on whether the treatment is experimental or investigative (including standards for concurrent review); exclusions based on failure to complete a course of treatment; and restrictions based on geographic location, facility type, provider specialty, and other criteria that limit the scope or duration of benefits for services provided under the plan or coverage.

The MHPAEA has been substantially amended since its initial enactment as the Mental Health Parity Act in September 1996. The Patient Protection and Affordable Care Act in 2010 allowed for application of the regulation to many health insurance plans that had previously been outside its scope. Notably, the Mental Health Parity Act has been expanded to cover substance use disorders.

However, despite efforts to allow for equal access to treatments for mental and physical disabilities, financial requirements, treatment limitations, and processes that evaluate annual and lifetime dollar limits for MH/SUD continue to be used. MHPAEA does not apply directly to small group health plans, and only applies to large group health plans and health insurance issuers that opt into policies that include MH/SUD benefits.

Much like QALY evaluation standards, the MHPAEA also considers likelihood of improvement of a medical condition. For instance, in the context of residential treatment of MH/SUD, MHPAEA requires the likelihood that inpatient treatment will result in improvement, and policies under this act cover only services that result in measurable and substantial improvement in mental health status within 90 days.

The MHPAEA also does not recognize certain experimental and investigative treatments that tend, in practice, to more adversely affect the availability of treatments for MH/SUD. For example, Autism Spectrum Disorder is categorized as a mental disability, and Applied Behavior Analysis (ABA) therapy has been professionally recognized as a method of treatment for children with the disorder. However, the NQTL is applied more stringently to MH/SUD, excluding these benefits under the MHPAEA.

Although both the ADA and MHPAEA facially prohibit discrimination on the basis of disability, the standards used to assess financial requirements and treatment limitations often-times have a disparate impact on chronic life-shortening and mental disabilities. Misapplication of the ADA and MHPAEA, and discrimination against certain individuals with disabilities, may lead to even more severe consequences, particularly in the case of mental disabilities.

E. QALY Creates a Risk of Institutionalization of Mentally Disabled Persons Which is Prohibited by the ADA through the Integration Mandate

The Attorney General, in issuing regulations implementing Title II of the ADA as directed by Congress, created the integration mandate.[23] The integration mandate states that: "A public entity shall administer services, programs, and activities in the most integrated setting appropriate to the needs of qualified individuals with disabilities."

The integration mandate reflects the need for heightened protection in preventing discrimination against mentally disabled persons in the form of segregation from others when receiving relevant treatment opportunities. The potential use of QALY to assess certain mental health treatments could narrow treatment options for the mentally disabled and thus heighten the possibility of segregation through community isolation or even institutionalization. A QALY-based ADA violation may be found if the reduced availability of treatments increases the risk of certain mentally disabled people requiring institutionalization. And although the integration mandate is significant for all individuals with disabilities, it may simply be more difficult to fully measure the impact of a mental health treatment on the quality of life of a person with such a disability, and thus, there must be further consideration for individuals with mental disabilities.

The standard for a mentally disabled person's full quality of life may be especially difficult to measure or for them to achieve. In those cases QALY's assignment of lower values for treatments of mental conditions may deny mentally ill persons Medicaid coverage and thereby render effective treatments unaffordable to them. As a result, their conditions may worsen, requiring them to reside in a specialized mental institution or otherwise be isolated from the community. If QALY's ratings result in greater Medicaid-funded availability of treatments for physical injuries, diseases, or disabilities, but could be seen to permit lesser medical benefits to mentally disabled persons, because of their disability, that is precisely the type of discrimination the ADA prohibits.

In one of the most influential cases interpreting the ADA, the Supreme Court found the administration of a service or program furnished by a public entity in a manner that increases the risk of institutionalization for mentally disabled persons to be a clear violation of the ADA due to the disparate impact on mentally disabled persons.[24] There is a significant likelihood that application of QALY would make treatments unavailable that would improve a mentally disabled person's condition but otherwise not return them to an unattainable full quality of life. Without these treatments, some mentally disabled persons would be at a higher risk of being institutionalized.

Even beyond that, though a public program or service that causes mentally disabled persons to receive care in a segregated institutionalized setting, while allowing the physically disabled to receive services in a community setting, is itself a violation of the ADA[25]. Undue institutionalization of the mentally disabled is discrimination under the ADA regardless of how everyone else is treated.[26]

And the reasoning that underpins the *Olmstead* decision has been expanded beyond just the institutionalization of mentally disabled persons. This presents a significant problem for the legality of QALY, compounded by the ADA's animating policy that empowers courts to construe its provisions broadly in order to effectuate its purpose.[27]

F. Adjusting QALY to Comply with the ADA Would Likely Undermine Its Cost-Saving Purpose

Unequal treatment *among* people with different disabilities is not per se discrimination under the ADA, so long as disabled individuals are not denied services provided to the able-bodied (or able-minded) on the basis of their disabilities. However, this unequal treatment is permissible only if a public entity administers a service or program to provide greater benefits to the disabled: "Nothing in this part prohibits a public entity from providing benefits, services, or advantages to individuals with disabilities, or to a particular class of individuals with disabilities beyond those required by this part."[28] Thus any adjustment to the QALY methodology that distinguished among different types of disabilities would be scrutinized, likely being upheld only if it provides a greater benefit to a class of disabled persons, and thus likelier than not to increase costs. Conversely, any cost-saving adjustment would likely be a violation in itself, if it was found to make any treatment less available or more expensive.

Conclusion

A definitive determination of whether QALY violates the ADA when applied to Medicaid patients cannot be obtained until it is implemented and challenged in court. There is nothing that can be done to prevent a lawsuit challenging QALY's compliance with the ADA, if it is incorporated into state Medicaid programs. A legal challenge on ADA grounds seems almost certain given the history of similar methodologies.

Nevertheless, it can be predicted with confidence that such use of QALY would violate the ADA on at least two separate, but related grounds. First, by decreasing the availability of effective treatments for disabled persons. Second, by increasing the risk of institutionalization of certain mentally disabled persons. Any cost-saving adjustment of QALY's methodology that makes certain treatments more expensive or less available would itself be a violation, even if done in an effort to comply with the ADA.

There are additional ADA grounds upon which QALY could be challenged that I have not addressed. These include, but are not limited to: the participation rates of both physically and mentally disabled persons in the surveys incorporated into QALY's valuations; the ability of mentally disabled persons to fully-comprehend and meaningfully participate in the surveys; and non-coverage of drugs that significantly improve the quality of life for individuals with conditions causing shortened life expectancy. These challenges may be brought by one qualified disabled individual that lost coverage for a treatment QALY deemed as "low value" or an entire class of similarly situated disabled persons.

In addition to ADA compliance issues, there is the possibility that QALY does not comply with the Medicaid Act. A separate analysis would be necessary to predict QALY's threshold legality under the Medicaid Act.

JIM MCKENNA, Senior Legal Scholar at Pioneer, provided invaluable assistance for the chapter on the impact of QALY on people living with disabilities. Jim's analysis of the Americans with Disabilities Act was particularly insightful.

CHAPTER 4

QALY and Cancer Treatments: An Ill-Advised Match

Cancer is a dreaded disease — perhaps the most dreaded. While the CDC reported that 659,041 Americans died of cardiovascular disease in 2019, cancer deaths were a close second at 599,601.[29] Despite being the second leading cause of death, cancer seems to strike with a certain randomness, at times impacting seemingly healthy people whose lifestyle, in many cases, appears not to be a factor in the onset of the disease.

Cardiovascular disease treatments and oncology treatments increasingly differ in their costs to the healthcare system. One recent study of healthcare claims data listed oncology as the number one therapeutic area for high-cost claims, making up 18 percent of them. The study also pointed out that oncologics were the most costly therapeutic class (non-discounted spending), spending on which had risen from $39.1 billion in 2015 to $67.5 billion in 2019.[30] In contrast, while there are some high-cost cardiovascular treatments, such as newer anticoagulants, many commonly prescribed cardiovascular treatments, such as numerous statins and antihypertensives, are low-cost generics.

While high spending levels on cancer treatments are an issue for the healthcare system, denying afflicted patients' access to innovative cancer therapies can be a political third rail. Most people know someone who has suffered from cancer, and they know the emotional fear and physical pain that can follow such a diagnosis. Denying certain treatments to oncology patients can be viewed, then, as enforcing a death sentence. Nonetheless, some researchers have waded into these perilous waters by conducting "health technology" assessments, or studies, that seek to weed out oncology therapies that are deemed "not cost-effective." In the United States, the Institute for Clinical and Economic Review (ICER) has "reviewed" a number of new cancer therapies and, in most cases, argued that these medicines were "not cost-effective." According to one study, ICER concluded that seven of the newest medicines should not be placed on health plan formularies unless they offered discounts of between 51 and 68 percent.[31]

President Biden has said that he learned, when head of the Obama administration's "Cancer Moonshot," that many cancer therapies are "abusively priced by manufacturers." Therefore, he has promised to have an "independent review board" assess the value of "specialized biotech drugs that have little or no competition to keep prices in check."[32]

Of course, by definition, this review board cannot possibly be "independent," as the President has already determined the outcome of the board's review, publicly arguing that the board's mission will be to cut the costs of biologics, especially cancer therapies, for payers such as the government. The political danger for the President will be the same danger that British policy makers ran into when, in 1999, they created the National Institute for Health and Care Excellence (NICE) to hold down drug costs in Britain's National Health Service (NHS). As noted in Chapter 1, a political firestorm erupted when it became clear that NICE's devaluation of new cancer therapies, and the denial of those treatments to the British people, had degraded the quality of Britain's oncology care.

The UK's Cancer Drugs Fund

QALY rates the value of a therapy according to its ability to extend life and to improve the quality of life. Many breakthrough cancer therapies may only extend the life of a patient by months, not years. For this reason, new cancer therapies have tended to get poor ratings in systems that use QALY, such as NICE's and ICER's.

The QALY criteria that are so controversial in rating the costs of cancer therapies was a British creation. Alan Williams, a professor of health economics at the University of York, began developing QALY in the late 1960s and 1970s.[33] By the mid-1990s, many British health policy experts, including members of the House of Commons' Health Committee, had embraced the idea that there are "four hurdles" a pharmaceutical needed to cross before it should be made available to the British public. To the traditional three hurdles — safety, quality of manufacture, and efficacy — a fourth hurdle was added: cost-effectiveness. Yet, at this early stage, how cost-effectiveness was to be measured had not yet been determined, and pharmaceutical companies began hiring health economists to make the case that their drugs were cost-effective.

As money got tighter in the National Health Service (NHS), health policy makers began to talk openly about the need to ration treatments. In fact, over the course of the 1990s, the influential *British Medical Journal* published 45 articles that discussed rationing. Had not rationing, after all, been a huge success in allocating resources during the Second World War? Throughout John Major's tenure as Prime Minister, the debate over funding for, and the sustainability of, the NHS was intense.

In a prelude to the creation of NICE, in 1995, then-Minister of State for Health Gerry Malone was asked to decide if the NHS would pay for Beta-interferon, a treatment that seemed to lessen the severity and frequency of attacks suffered by multiple sclerosis (MS) patients. It was estimated that the cost of Beta-interferon for all of Britain's 70,000 MS patients would be as high as £380 million, or 10 percent of the total NHS budget. Like Solomon, Malone tried to cut the baby in half, allowing the use of Beta-interferon but discouraging its widespread adoption. Malone, however, was unhappy about being forced to make such a life-and-death decision, and he tasked his staff with developing a system whereby politicians like himself would not be placed in this difficult position again.

While NICE was not created by Malone's team, it was during his tenure that the idea of some type of cost-effectiveness referee gained traction among British policymakers.

Then came Tony Blair's landslide election in 1997 on a platform to "save the National Health Service." One way to accomplish this was to create some type of body to rate the value of treatments and reduce the NHS's purchase of ineffective ones. The trade association for pharmaceutical firms, the British Pharmaceutical Industry (BPI), generally supported the creation of such a body because the NHS at that time had a decentralized system of pharmaceutical access, with some regions permitting the use of new drugs and others restricting them. The BPI felt that a competent body of professionals would make access to new drugs more uniform across the whole system. This was a profound misjudgment on the part of industry.

It was Frank Dobson, Blair's minister of state for health, who came up with the name "NICE," standing for the "National Institute for Clinical Excellence." In July of 1998, the government published *A First Class Service*, the road map for the use of NICE to "improve" quality in the NHS by providing "authoritative guidance…for all health professionals on the latest drugs and technologies."[34]

Initially, British policy makers were not sure if NICE would increase or decrease NHS spending. The hope was that it would rationalize spending and steer the healthcare community toward the most cost-effective treatments, thereby increasing quality and affordability.

So, NICE began doing reviews and rendering judgment on therapies such as the removal of wisdom teeth, flu treatments, and coronary stents. NICE first got into hot water in 2000 when it judged two treatments for multiple sclerosis, Beta-interferon and glatiramer acetate, as not worth the benefit and costs. The result was exactly the kind of firestorm Gerry Malone had sought to avoid in his earlier decision on Beta-interferon. MS patients in wheelchairs swarmed the House of Commons, and the MS Society took out newspaper ads condemning the decision. NICE held fast, but Tony Blair was not happy with the political fallout.

He instructed the NHS to negotiate with manufacturers and, with a price cut, some access was restored to patients.

Then came Herceptin. The novel breast cancer drug had its clinical trials canceled early because the data were so strong; it was viewed as unethical to keep people in trials taking placebo. The head of the American Society of Clinical Oncology (ASCO) declared Herceptin to be the greatest breakthrough in breast cancer treatment in 30 years.

While Herceptin had been approved for end-stage breast cancer and metastatic breast cancer, it had not yet been evaluated by NICE for early-stage breast cancer. And British women wanted it, despite the fact that its manufacturer had not even applied to the EU for a license for early-stage cancer. Nonetheless, the stories of these women, desperate for Herceptin, filled the media. Petitions were delivered to 10 Downing Street and marches on Parliament were organized.

The media narrative on Herceptin became twofold. First, the NHS had overspent its budget such that it could not pay for the breakthrough drug. The second, and more plausible problem, was that NICE was terribly slow at conducting evaluations, sometimes taking more than two years to review a new drug. Reviewing cancer therapies, in particular, tended to be slower since NICE wanted to collect data on overall survival (OS) rates, data that did not typically emerge from clinical trials because of the extended time period generally required to determine length of survival.

Under political pressure, the politicians caved. The Health Secretary ordered the NHS to give Herceptin to early-stage patients in order to evaluate its effectiveness. However, NICE's leaders, as well as other health policy experts, viewed this decision as an emasculation of NICE by politicians who were agreeing to offer a drug without a review or a license due to political pressure. The tabloid press disagreed and accused NICE of literally killing patients. As the battle raged, the EU finally provided a license for Herceptin for early-stage breast cancer and the NHS agreed to cover it. The Herceptin controversy, however, was a window into what was to come.

The next struggle was over an Alzheimer's drug, and then a treatment for macular degeneration. With each review, it became clear that QALY had become the standard instrument of assessing value and that the "threshold" for rating a drug as cost-effective, £20,000–£30,000 per QALY, was likely to result in determining many new drugs were not cost-effective.

With the NHS budget growing, and pharmaceutical companies developing ever more expensive cancer therapies, there was pressure on NICE to act. NHS began delaying payment for new oncology products until NICE had completed its reviews. Furthermore, the NHS — unwisely it seems — informed patients that if they paid for yet-to-be approved drugs out of their own pockets, the NHS would not pay for any of their overall care. When the media discovered incidents of this, the stories put the NHS in a very unfavorable light.

Around the same time, NICE conducted a review of four new kidney cancer drugs. Although the drugs were ruled "clinically effective," they were determined to be "not cost-effective" because they violated QALY thresholds. Then, after the kidney cancer reviews, the political dam was completely broken by a study comparing Great Britain's spending on cancer care with that of 14 other countries. The report concluded that, for Great Britain to reach the average per capita spending on cancer care among the countries studied, the NHS would need to increase its spending on cancer care by £200 million per year.

Conservative Party politicians quickly proposed a fund that would pay for new cancer drugs whether or not NICE had reviewed them. The Cancer Drugs Fund was allocated a budget, probably not coincidentally, of £200 million. The Conservative Party leader, David Cameron, announced the idea for the Cancer Drugs Fund in 2010 after learning about the plight of a constituent who had been denied a kidney cancer drug.

Embraced by physicians, patients, and the pharmaceutical industry, the Cancer Drugs Fund was a great political success. While many economists and NICE supporters were downright hostile, arguing that it was an inefficient waste of money, the reality is that the Fund won the support of the British public because NICE, and its use of the low-threshold QALY, had degraded the quality of cancer care in Britain. David Cameron could say, with some truth, that "other European countries are doing better than us at giving people longer, happier lives with cancer… and in the UK today there are some people — some thousands of people — who want a certain drug, whose doctors tell them they should have a certain cancer drug, who don't get it."[35]

The narrative of Britain's experience with NICE contains almost perfectly crystallized examples of the political dynamics that can occur when governments embrace cost-effectiveness reviews for oncology products. The first dynamic was demonstrated by Gerry Malone: politicians do not want to make decisions to deny specific therapies to patients. Instead, they want to fob those decisions onto a supposedly independent body of experts who can assure the public that the decision was made based on "objective" criteria.

The second dynamic, most prominent in government-funded healthcare systems, is that the entities charged with assessing cost-effectiveness increasingly lean toward denying access to new medicines. Government healthcare programs tend to exhibit budgetary stress because free or low-cost care tends to drive higher utilization. Therefore, governments create cost-effectiveness functions to justify limiting utilization of new technologies.

The entities charged with assessing cost-effectiveness understand that their mission is to label certain purchases as not cost-effective and that their role, whatever else it might be, is not to justify increases in spending. In short, the deck becomes stacked toward restricting access to new medicines.

These are useful lessons when considering ICER's assessment of the value of oncology treatments, as ICER's methodology tends to rate cancer drugs in a way that discounts their value. The Cancer Drugs Fund backstory is one that should be read by policy makers in the Biden administration who seem to be embracing a cost-effectiveness review of biologics — likely to include many new cancer drugs.

Problems with ICER and QALY in Evaluating Oncology Therapeutics

The use of QALY poses multiple problems that become apparent when reviews of oncology products are published. While withholding cancer treatments based on economic modeling has obvious ethical implications, here I largely restrict discussion to the methodological and contextual shortcomings of QALY in evaluating cancer therapies.

1. The Societal Benefits of Effective Oncologics: A Disease of Families

When a person is diagnosed with cancer, the burden is not simply on the patient, but falls on the whole family. Studies indicate, for example, that a typical caregiver for a cancer patient provides an average of a staggering 32.9 hours of care per week.[36] Not unexpectedly, this takes a toll on caregivers, who experience very high rates of depression, anxiety and insomnia.[37, 38, 39]

One would expect the value of any therapy that ameliorates the tremendous burden on caregivers to reflect this significant benefit. Yet, ICER does not include indirect benefits in its value assessments. Instead, over the years, as it became apparent that assigning no value within its assessments to caregiver sacrifices seemed flawed and ill-conceived, ICER conceded the value of some of these social benefits yet did not go so far as to actually incorporate that value into its models.

ICER obliquely and opaquely hinted it may consider the societal benefits of a therapy when the societal cost is large.[40] In other words, patient advocates should try to make the case that these caregivers matter, and ICER may consider it. But, no promises. ICER does this in many situations when its frameworks have obvious flaws, such as low QALY thresholds for rare disease drugs, where it has hinted at considering higher thresholds for certain therapies. But the more inferred concessions ICER makes, the more subjective its frameworks appear.

The reason that ICER does not include the clear societal benefits of certain treatments is obvious: consideration of such data would result in more treatments being rated as cost-effective. For example, one study demonstrated that the inclusion of economic productivity gains resulting from a given therapy would result in a higher value for the therapy. "The exclusion of productivity costs can alter, often underestimating, the assessment of value."[41] That same study pointed out that although ICER has nodded to the inclusion of societal benefit values in its reviews: "Since March 2017, 18 of 19 (94.7%) pharmaceutical value assessment reports from the Institute for Clinical and Economic Review included productivity costs in the report, but only 2 (11.1%) included productivity in a primary (co-base case) analysis."

Patient groups, patients, and families who get frustrated at the dodginess of ICER's framework need to keep in mind that ICER is not an independent, objective actor. ICER was originally formed by the health insurance industry with one goal in mind: lower its drug costs to increase its profits. ICER's roots therefore are not found in an academic body seeking to ascertain the true "value" of therapies; all its cost-effectiveness reviews need to be understood in this light.

2. Oncology Clinical Trial Results Do Not Reflect the Patient Population Who Will Use the Medicine and Measure Progression-Free Survival (PFS), not Overall Survival (OS)

ICER cost-effectiveness reviews are typically based on clinical trial data. This is a particular problem when evaluating cancer treatments since the clinical trial population in an oncology trial is not representative of the population who will actually take the medicine. A very recent report from the Congressional Research Service "has shown that more than half of oncology drug use is off-label."[42] By definition, when drugs are used off-label, they are not being used for the conditions for which they have been FDA-approved and labeled. Consequently, the data that ICER uses to conduct a cost-effectiveness review on a treatment is projectable to less than half of the population that will actually use the medicine.

Not only is ICER studying data from patients who do not represent the full population who will use the medicine, the clinical trial exclusion criteria allows for the accrual of a very narrow patient dataset. The comorbidities that preclude trial eligibility are often those that afflict many cancer patients who are typically elderly and at higher risk than the study population. As Richard Pazdur and his coauthors commented: "Although eligibility criteria are needed to define the study population and improve safety, overly restrictive eligibility criteria limit participation in clinical trials, cause the study population to be unrepresentative of the general population of patients with cancer, and limit patient access to new treatments."[43]

Moreover, the QALY methodology used by ICER measures Overall Survival (OS), or how long a patient survives, while most oncology clinical trials measure Progression Free Survival (PFS), the length of time a patient lives with a disease during and after treatment without the disease getting worse (see p. 28 for more). Therefore, economic evaluations of oncology therapies must make guesses about OS based upon PFS trial data. As one study put the problem, "QALYs rely on evidence of improvements in overall survival (OS), and clinical trials rarely run long enough to establish that…Consequently, the use of clinical trial evidence in cost-effectiveness studies requires analysts to estimate OS on the basis of intermediate endpoints such as PFS, time to progression, etc."[44] In other words, QALY is ill-suited to value cancer therapies using clinical trial data alone.

One new study[45] has pointed out that people of color are substantially underrepresented in oncology clinical trials, further calling into question QALY studies that rely on clinical trial data. "Oncology is particularly illustrative of this systemic inequity. In a review of recruitment in phase 3 cancer clinical trials conducted between 2001 and 2010, reviewers found that just 6.2% were African American; in contrast to studies conducted between 1990 and 2000, in which 10.5% were African American. This illustrates that despite awareness of the problem that RCTs are highly homogeneous, efforts to enroll African Americans appear to have diminished or become less effective over the last two decades."

The study goes on to argue that ICER's methodology therefore discriminates against people of color in assessing the value of therapies that this patient population desperately needs. "This failure to power clinical trials to yield statistically significant results for patients of color compromises the clinical validity of data and information regarding disease presentation and therapeutic responses and findings regarding safety and efficacy. By extension, methodologies designed and employed by health economists to assess the relative value of health technologies are equally compromised and discreditable." While it is important to have ethnic diversity in clinical trial participation, it also may be advantageous to seek out lower-income populations for participation irregardless of ethnicity.

3. Discounting of Patient Preferences

When estimating QALYs, as has been discussed, cost-effectiveness studies assess the ability of a treatment both to extend life and to improve the quality of life. Measuring health-related quality of life (HRTQoL) is a two-step process. First, patients are given "patient reported outcomes" (PRO) questionnaires, in which they report changes in their quality of life. From the perspective of a cancer patient, the next step is where the process is fundamentally flawed. "Weight…is attached to each aspect of HRQoL *from the perspective (by convention) of the general public*, in order to summarize the PRO data provided by patients."[46]

In other words, the value assigned to any improvements in various aspects of a patient's quality of life are not provided by surveying patients themselves who live with their illness, but by members of the general public, who must imagine the value, for example, of a substantial reduction in pain. The rationale for using general population opinions is that, "the views of the general public, as taxpayers and potential patients…should be taken into account in decisions which affect the allocation of public sector budgets…"[47]

There seems to be, however, another reason why cost-effectiveness studies are not based on patient experiences when valuing quality of life improvements. It is because patients would likely value these improvements more highly than the general public, leading, in the final analysis, to more therapies being rated as cost-effective. Surveys of the general public do not accurately reflect the values actual cancer patients tend to place on incremental improvements in their quality of life, because patients tend to value improvements in their health more highly than do non-patients.

As explained by the Office of Health Economics, London, UK, "the practice of using valuations of members of the general population, as recommended by NICE, is problematic because such individuals typically display a misunderstanding of what it is really like for patients to live with cancer."[48]

One large study of the differences between evaluations made by the general public and those made by patients concluded that surveys of the general public tended to accord less value to treatments that may extend life than to therapies that restore performance: "the use of general population values rather than patient values tend to favor interventions aimed at achieving perfect functioning whilst disfavouring life-prolonging interventions."[49] For obvious reasons, discounting life-prolonging interventions is contrary to the goals of most patients with cancer.

4. The Challenge of Personalized Medicine

With the mapping of the human genome, medical science is discovering that many disease states are gene related. This is particularly true in oncology, where patients with certain genetic profiles respond differently to different therapies. For some patients, a particular therapy is highly effective and has few side effects, while for other patients, it does not work at all. As noted on Cancer.net, the patient information website of the American Society of Clinical Oncologists (ASCO): "(R)esearchers began finding genetic differences in people and their cancers. These differences explained a great deal about why cancers responded differently to the same treatment."[50]

Genetically targeted cancer therapies, often referred to as

personalized medicine, are becoming more and more common. The ASCO website mentions that targeted treatments are available for the following cancer types: bladder cancer, brain cancer, breast cancer, cervical cancer, colorectal cancer, endometrial cancer, esophageal cancer, head and neck cancer, gastrointestinal stromal tumor (GIST), kidney cancer, leukemia, liver cancer, lymphoma, lung cancer, melanoma, multiple myeloma, neuroblastoma, neuroendocrine tumors, pancreatic cancer, prostate cancer, soft tissue sarcoma, stomach cancer, and thyroid cancer. The Personalized Medicine Coalition calculated that 25% of drug approvals between 2015 and 2018 were for personalized medicines.[51] It pointed out to ICER that "A population-level framework may encourage the restriction of access to a new drug based on reported averages, which limits treatment options available to individual patients who may have benefitted from them."[52]

In other words, if personalized medicines are deemed not cost-effective by a value framework, access may be prevented even for patients who, because of their genetic profile, may respond exceptionally well to a certain therapy. As a study in the Journal of Clinical Pathways put the problem: "If the application of the framework is not sufficiently personalized, then the value determination applies only to the average patient, not specific ones."[53]

The Multiple Myeloma Research Foundation pointed out "the promise of precision medicine is that each patient is unique and will consequently respond to treatment differently based on their particular genetic profile and further understanding of the biology of their disease."[54] This statement came in 2016 in response to the first of multiple reviews ICER has conducted[55] over a number of years on treatments for multiple myeloma.

In its first review in 2016, ICER had a difficult time conducting its cost-effectiveness analysis because of the varying profiles of multiple myeloma patients. After reading ICER's report, one physician concluded that ICER had "come to understand that each patient is unique and different and that all therapies will be required during the course of multiple relapses."[56] Despite this recognition, however, and the promise of the new breakthrough targeted-therapies that had become available by 2016, ICER concluded that "at current wholesale acquisition costs, the estimated long-term cost-effectiveness of these regimens exceeds commonly cited thresholds." According to ICER, none of the new breakthrough treatments were rated "high value."[57]

In 2016, ICER also released a report on treatments for non-small cell lung cancer. The report generated great criticism from the oncology community. According to one group of highly regarded oncologists: "Based upon our reviews of this report, ICER appears to represent a perspective that is less oriented towards patient benefit than towards motivations that would limit patient access to new therapeutic options. ICER's clinico-economic methods include approaches and metrics that, due to their singular focus on population-level health, would likely fail patients on an individual, clinical needs basis."[58]

Since these controversial 2016 reviews, ICER has seemed to put more focus on treatments for certain subgroups of cancer patients. However, as discussed below, this has not resulted in more favorable value assessments for targeted treatments. Between 2016 and 2019, ICER reviewed 11 new cancer therapies and concluded that only four were "cost-effective."

5. QALYs Represent a Poor Measure of Progress Against Cancer

Progress against cancer is measured in increments. A key outcome metric is "progression-free survival (PFS)", which is: "The length of time during and after the treatment of a disease, such as cancer, that a patient lives with the disease but it does not get worse. In a clinical trial, measuring progression-free survival is one way to see how well a new treatment works."[59] Typically, advances in PFS are measured in months, not years, so PFS9 indicates that for 9 months of a patient's life the cancer did not get worse.

Given that progress against cancer is measured in months, not years, QALY tends to be an inappropriate metric for new cancer therapies because their impact, while clinically meaningful, does not often extend longevity for years. As noted by the authors of *Limitations of QALY: A Literature Review*, "The QALY metric has also been critiqued for having insufficient sensitivity to measure small but meaningful changes in health status — or utility. Such changes in health status are particularly applicable (and important) to certain patient subgroups, for example, cancer patients where multiple studies have outlined a need for additional dimensions to be considered."[60]

This tendency of ICER to undervalue cancer therapies was documented in a 2020 study published in *The Lancet* that examined ICER's cost-effectiveness reviews completed between 2016 and 2019, for 11 cancer drugs. As mentioned at the end of the previous section, of the 11 drugs, only four were rated as cost-effective and therefore "recommended for formulary inclusion at the stated list price."[61] The study concluded that, for the other seven drugs to be recommended for formulary inclusion, manufacturer list prices would need to fall 51 percent to achieve the goal of $150,000 per QALY and 68 percent to achieve $100,000 per QALY.

Moreover, the authors of this *Lancet* study concluded that, because the UK's NHS can negotiate substantial discounts from manufacturers, its cost-effectiveness body, NICE, is more likely to rate new cancer drugs as cost-effective than ICER. "Our analysis shows that NICE's capacity to negotiate price discounts and access schemes results in much lower cost per QALY valuations and more favourable recommendations than those of ICER for similarly assessed cancer drugs."[62] The study authors concluded that "the QALY, because of the way it is constructed, may indeed fail to accurately capture the value of the health gains that are deemed important by cancer patients."

Conclusion

Cancer death rates have been declining for a number of decades. Between 2001 and 2017, cancer death rates declined by 1.8 percent for men and 1.4 percent for women.[63] However, the COVID crisis could see that progress reversed. The American Society of Clinical Oncology reports that among Americans scheduled for a cancer screening test such as a mammogram, colonoscopy, skin check, or Pap/HPV test during the pandemic, "nearly two-thirds, or 64%, reported that it was delayed or canceled."[64]

In other words, we could see cancer death rates rise for the first time in decades. The only way to offset this increase is for Americans to return to regular cancer screenings, and to allow those diagnosed to have access to the latest, most advanced treatments. For those covered by payers who apply ICER's framework for evaluating cancer treatments, access could be precluded.

To improve ICER's framework, possible reforms include allowing actual patients to make value determinations, rather than members of the general public; including societal benefits in its primary analysis; and raising QALY thresholds for certain serious cancer treatments.

The problem, of course, is that ICER is highly unlikely to enact such reforms. Its mission is not to conduct "objective" evaluations of treatments that could offer help and hope to very sick people. Rather, it seeks to limit patient access to expensive new treatments and reduce drug costs for payers.

There seems to be a certain naiveté on the part of some policymakers, and some in industry; they think ICER can be "persuaded" to accept major revisions to its framework. Sadly, however, ICER's goal is not to adopt the best possible framework for patients and their families. ICER is focused on creating leverage for payers in their pricing negotiations with manufacturers. Only certain very limited concessions are likely to be accepted by ICER in adapting its framework.

ICER has rejected patient group suggestions for reforms, such as allowing actual patient's to establish the value parameters for quality of life improvements. Given its unwillingness to accept reforms that are advocated by patients, as well as the inadequacy of QALY in evaluating the cost-effectiveness of cancer therapies, policy makers should not waste time trying to convince ICER to modify its framework methodology. Instead, policy makers would be wise to adopt the David Cameron strategy of banning use of QALY altogether in evaluating cancer treatments and prohibit ICER from advising U.S. government agencies regarding their formulary designs.[65]

Some policy makers will recoil from this approach and argue that the cancer treatment cost growth is unsustainable and rigorous cost-effectiveness evaluations should be a priority. However, the data do not support the notion of unsustainable cost growth in the short term. According to consulting firm IQVIA, "Brand losses of exclusivity are projected to have a $139 billion negative impact on brand sales from 2020–2024, compared to the $107 billion impact seen from 2014–2019." As a result, patent expirations during this five-year window will make new oncologics quite affordable to the healthcare system. The IQVIA report also points out that: "Manufacturer net prices are expected to grow between 1% and –2% in the United States over the next five years, significantly below historic levels."[66]

Given the possible growth in cancer incidence because of reduced screenings during the COVID pandemic, as well as the coming patent expirations on huge selling drugs such as Januvia, Humira, Victoza, and Vyvanse, now is not the time to restrict access. On the contrary, we should be incenting companies to invest more in discovering better treatments. The control and cure of cancer, to save lives in this and the next generation, can only be achieved through the discovery of novel treatments. And, let's face it, restricting access to new therapies that can reduce suffering is both cruel and morally unacceptable.

CHAPTER 5

Looming Challenges for ICER in Assessing the Value of Rare Disease Therapies

Led by the United Kingdom's National Institute for Health and Care Excellence (NICE), many developed countries with nationalized healthcare systems have traditionally relied on cost-effectiveness reviews to rate emerging therapies and make decisions about whether to cover those treatments in their health systems. As I've noted throughout this book, the NICE methodology uses QALYs to rate the value of drugs and devices based upon their ability to extend life and to improve the quality of life.

Supporters argue that QALY-based reviews represent an objective and balanced method of assessing the true value of new treatments and provide policy makers with an indispensable cost control tool. Critics argue that the reviews are simply a poorly constructed fig leaf to justify rationing and deny treatments to vulnerable populations such as the elderly, the disabled, cancer patients, and those with rare diseases. A number of critics see the slow degradation of oncology care in the United Kingdom as the clearest example of QALY's failure, because Parliament was forced to ignore the NICE cost-effectiveness reviews and pay for cancer drugs regardless of their QALY rating.[67]

In the United States, ICER is working to bring these European-style cost-effectiveness reviews to commercial and government payers. Like NICE, ICER employs QALY methodology. During consideration of the Affordable Care Act, Congress worried about the impact of these reviews on the elderly and disabled and made it illegal to use QALY methodology in cost-effectiveness reviews for Medicare. ICER's ambition therefore shifted to having state Medicaid programs and commercial plans employ its reviews when making coverage decisions. CVS Caremark, the nation's second largest pharmacy benefit manager, recently announced that it would employ QALY-based analysis to assist clients in lowering drug costs, although it is unclear if the company still intends to move forward with the plan.[68]

In previous chapters, I used the significant academic literature extant on the limitations of QALY methodology to highlight its potential adverse impacts upon various patient populations.[69] In this chapter, I will focus on the potential obsolescence of QALY methodology in conducting cost-effectiveness reviews on the most rapidly growing sector of the biopharmaceutical marketplace: therapies for rare and orphan diseases.

ORPHAN DRUGS ARE ROUGHLY DEFINED AS: drugs intended to treat a patient universe of 200,000 patients or less; orphan indications likewise is a new indication for an existing drug that is meant to treat a patient population of 200,000 or less.

The Changing Biopharmaceutical Marketplace

For a variety of complex policy, legal, regulatory and scientific reasons, the pharmaceutical marketplace has seen a dramatic change of direction in recent decades. FDA approvals for new orphan drugs[70] or new orphan indications have exploded. For example, FDA-approved orphan indications grew from two in 1983 to 80 in 2017. As the IQVIA Institute pointed out: "In just 2017 alone, the FDA granted orphan designations to over 429 unique drugs under development."[71] The laboratories of biopharmaceutical companies are increasingly focused on orphan drugs and for the first time, in 2018, more than half of new drug approvals were for orphan drugs.

A related trend in the biopharmaceutical marketplace is the growth in spending on specialty drugs. Specialty products have no exact definition but are typically drugs that treat complex conditions, such as cancer or rheumatoid arthritis, and generally are not delivered in pill form, but may be infused or injected. Eighty-seven percent of orphan drugs fall into the specialty drug category, but many specialty drugs have patient populations larger than 200,000 and do not enjoy orphan drug status. That said, specialty drugs generally have smaller patient populations, and are more expensive than traditional small molecule drugs. For example, while an estimated 1.3 million people in the U.S. suffer from rheumatoid arthritis typically treated with specialty medicines, 95 million Americans have high cholesterol that is typically treated with traditional small-molecule medicines.[72,73]

Specialty drugs, with orphan drugs as a subcategory, are responsible for the lion's share of spending on new drugs. In 2017, for example, net new spending on branded drugs was $12 billion, with specialty medicines making up $9.7 billion of that total. Of the 42 new medicines launched during 2017, 32 were specialty drugs.[74] Both specialty and orphan drugs are considerably more expensive than traditional medicines. One study predicted that, by 2023, the median annual prices of orphan and oncology drugs will be "well above" $100,000.[75] Overall, the specialty share of drug spending has grown from 11 percent in 1997 to 43 percent in 2017, while orphan drug spending grew from 4 percent to 11 percent over the same period.[76]

It should be noted that despite the higher prices for specialty and orphan drugs, there are data to suggest that the U.S. healthcare system is able to sustain these prices because many traditional blockbuster small-molecule medicines, such as Lipitor to treat high cholesterol, have gone off patent, generating enormous savings for the system.[77] Patent expirations provided $95 billion in savings in recent years, with $26 billion in savings coming in 2019 alone.

These savings from patent losses are so large because generic prescribing has increased dramatically. When doctors prescribe medicines for chronic conditions, about 90 percent of the time, patients will receive a generic drug, i.e. a traditional medicine that has gone off patent.[78] In other words, an accurate assessment of pharmaceutical spending growth should weigh the increases observed in speciality drug spending against the decreases in spending for small molecules. In short, for the foreseeable future, the growth in specialty and orphan drugs will not be an undue burden upon the healthcare system.

Specialty spending should also be weighed in the context of the level of innovation being brought to market. Many new specialty products offer breakthrough efficacy to patient populations who previously had few and suboptimal treatment options. The value to the patient of gene therapies for hereditary blindness or spinomuscular atrophy should not be underestimated.

Implications for Cost-Effectiveness Reviews

Since most of the growth in medical spending derives from specialty and orphan drugs, we must ensure that cost-effectiveness reviews are particularly well suited to evaluating drugs for smaller patient populations with complex and rare diseases. The question I attempt to address in this chapter is: Do traditional European style cost-effectiveness reviews, such as ICER's use of QALYs, lend themselves well to evaluating these new drugs?

Before 2017, even ICER itself would have answered this question in the negative. In that year it launched a review to revise its framework for evaluating drugs for "ultra-rare" diseases. In a press release requesting public comment on a revised framework, ICER acknowledged the unique challenges inherent in evaluating the growing number of drugs for complex diseases for smaller patient populations.[79] ICER wanted its revised framework for these drugs to reflect "the distinctive practical and ethical challenges associated with potential major advances for serious ultra-rare conditions."

The Traditional ICER Cost-Effectiveness Framework

Before we explore ICER's revised framework for rare disease drugs, we should examine its traditional framework. As with NICE in the UK, the bedrock methodology of ICER's framework is the QALY. As previously noted, a QALY rating combines two measurements of a drug's effectiveness into a single score: the drug's ability to prolong life and its ability to improve the quality of life. As explained by scholars in the *British Medical Bulletin*: "The QALY is able to combine the effects of health interventions on mortality and morbidity into a single index, thereby providing a 'common currency' to enable comparisons across different disease areas."[80]

QALY methodology ranks quality of life on a scale of 0 to 1, with zero being death and 1 being a year lived in perfect health. If a drug provides a quality of life ranked at .5, this is multiplied by the drug's longevity score. So a drug with a .5 quality of life score that provided for 4 additional years of life would receive a QALY score of 2 QALYs (.5 x 4). This score can then be compared with other treatments in the same category as well as with treatments for other conditions to evaluate the "value" of a new drug.

ICER's methodology next sets a "threshold" monetary value of a year of life lived in perfect health. To establish this threshold, ICER employs a recommendation from the World Health Organization (WHO) "which suggests a threshold range of 1–3 times the per capita GDP of the country per additional QALY. For the US, this translates to $57,000 to $171,000 per QALY gained, which is in close proximity to ICER's threshold of $50,000 to $150,000 per QALY gained."[81]

By combining a drug's longevity/quality of life score with the monetary threshold amounts, ICER assigns a relative value to different therapies. A drug that can provide a full year of life lived in perfect health for $50,000 or less is considered a "high value" treatment. A drug costing more than $150,000 provides for "low value" and a drug costing between $50,000 and $150,000 represents an "intermediate value" drug. While there are many questions about the appropriateness of this methodology for rating any pharmaceutical treatment, QALY is particularly ill-suited to assess the value of rare disease treatments for a variety of reasons discussed below.[82]

Thresholds Not Appropriate for Rare-Disease Drugs

With the Orphan Drug Act in 1983, Congress recognized that the traditional pharmaceutical business model was not producing enough therapies for rare diseases. The simple economic reason for this scarcity of rare disease drugs was that companies were sinking their substantial R&D budgets into therapeutic areas with higher prevalence rates, i.e. more potential customers. With the Orphan Drug Act, Congress provided greater market exclusivity, tax breaks, and other incentives to make R&D investment in rare disease drugs potentially more profitable. So began a trend of more and more drug approvals for rare disease and orphan drugs.

However, while federal law provided the impetus to invent more rare disease drugs, it did not solve the challenge of pricing them. R&D costs for developing and testing a rare disease drug are considerable, as finding and enrolling patients in trials are particularly challenging. And, with lower prevalence rates, the higher costs are spread over much smaller patient populations, making the price for one course of treatment substantially higher than traditional small-molecule drugs for large patient populations.

With the unique nature of rare diseases in mind, one 2014 study in the *Journal of Comparative Effectiveness Research* predicted that new cost-effectiveness models would need to be developed.[83] Without new models, the study predicted that traditional cost-effectiveness tools would be biased against rare disease drugs, leading to uniformly poor ratings. As the study pointed out, "given the largely fixed (i.e. independent from sales volume) nature of R&D costs, it seems plausible that the issue of not meeting conventional benchmarks for cost-effectiveness will only increase in relevance with decreasing prevalence rates, especially with drugs developed to treat small patient populations." The study's analysis turned out to be quite prescient. By 2018, a study appeared in *Health Affairs* that examined ICER's 2014–18 reviews of rare disease drugs to ascertain the number of therapies that had been rated as having "high value."[84] The answer was none. Of the five drugs evaluated to treat diseases for small populations, four were rated of "low value" while one was rated an "intermediate value."

The trend in the model's bias against rare disease drugs has continued. A very recent ICER review of two breakthrough therapies for Spinal Muscular Atrophy (SMA), a terrible childhood disease, concluded that neither therapy met "traditional cost-effectiveness thresholds."[85]

One option to mitigate or even eliminate this bias would be for ICER to raise its QALY thresholds for orphan or rare disease drugs. In general, ICER has refused to take this step, as, one might surmise, revising the thresholds based upon certain important contextual factors would open up the entire ICER methodology to the question of why certain key contextual issues for different disease states and patient populations are not already built into the model.

ICER has, however, created a new "ultra-rare" category of diseases with fewer than 10,000 patients, a category that does not exist in the current U.S. regulatory or legal framework. For this category, as the *Health Affairs* study explains, "ICER also presents in its reports additional cost-effectiveness benchmarks up to $500,000-per-QALY gained, stating that decision-makers may be willing to consider higher benchmarks in such situations." In other words, ICER is not raising the QALY threshold of cost-effectiveness to $500,000, it is merely willing to consider raising it in individual cases. As the recent SMA review demonstrated, however, ICER has not implemented a substantially new model for "ultra-rare" disease drugs.

Clinical Trial Data Too Limited to Evaluate Ultimate Value

Another factor in the emerging biopharmaceutical marketplace portends obsolescence of the QALY model: With the rising number of orphan or rare disease therapies, fewer patients are involved in clinical trials and the datasets are less robust than for other traditional drugs. This is particularly the case with what ICER classifies as "ultra-rare disease" drugs (URDs). As the study in the *Journal of Comparative Effectiveness Research* pointed out, less clinical research with URDs means "limited clinical understanding," fewer physicians with "specialized expertise," fewer "validated instruments to measure disease severity/progression," less ability to "accurately diagnose patients with URDs," and given the geographic dispersal of the small number of patients, the need to establish "multiple clinical trial sites" for those few patients.[86] In short, it is harder to generate robust clinical data for these diseases and therefore the data are less certain.

When it comes to confronting this problem of limited data, ICER likes to have it both ways. First, ICER is eager to point out the uncertainty inherent in the clinical data for rare disease drugs. In its recent review of two SMA therapies, for example, ICER points out that: "First, for both interventions, the narrow eligibility criteria of trials and the limited sample size…raise concerns about generalizability of results to the wider population of patients with SMA…In addition, there is a lack of data on the long-term safety and efficacy of both interventions.[87]" It goes on to point out that, also because of limited data, there is uncertainty about the potential for serious side effects or whether the therapies will be effective over the longer term.

Yet while ICER seems eager to point out that, because the safety and efficacy data is less robust for these two SMA therapies, their clinical value is less certain, ICER nonetheless seems confident in its assessment that neither drug is cost-effective, and that their prices should be far lower. How can one cast doubt on the reliability of the clinical evidence of effectiveness and safety and also confidently argue that they are overpriced? Isn't it also possible that the therapies are more effective and safer than the limited data indicate?

Rather than discouraging payers from covering new rare disease therapies, as ICER does, would not a more humane and prudent approach be to encourage payers to cover these drugs immediately in order to generate more data and reach a more certain cost-effectiveness conclusion, using real world evidence? In the case of Zolgensma, Novartis's drug or SMA, ICER issued its conclusion that the drug was not cost-effective on the same day the drug was approved by the FDA.[88] If payers accepted ICER's findings as stated, patients with this devastating condition would have been denied a chance at a treatment that could change the course and duration of their lives. ICER seems less eager to base its conclusions on robust data than to signal to payers that rare disease drugs are not a good value.

The Obsolescence of ICER's Model Will Increase with Genetic Advances

In the future, the practice of medicine will become increasingly personalized, and medicines will be targeted to patients based upon their genetic makeup. Diagnostic tests, not QALYs, will determine when a medicine is cost-effective. As one study in the *Journal of Stem Cell Research and Therapy* explains: "As we embark on a paradigm shift away from conventional medicine and it's intuitive 'one-size-fits-all' approach toward precision (or personalized) medicine, which utilizes an array of patient metrics including gene expression, metabolomics and predictive biomarkers, there will be an associated decrease in the level of variation in response to treatment."[89]

ICER's methodology is, by definition, a "one-size-fits-all" approach that will inevitably fail to keep up with medical science's understanding of how and why different therapies work differently for different patients. In the long run, ICER reviews will unlikely provide valuable insights into the cost-effectiveness of numerous therapies when those therapies will be understood to present a huge number of variations in patient responses due to complex genetic and metabolomic factors. As the Biotechnology Industry Organization pointed out in its comments on ICER's proposed framework for ultra-rare diseases: "A QALY distills the entire patient experience for a particular medical intervention into one number. But as the field of personalized medicine advances and interventions can be tailored down to the level of the patient's own genetic code, any rationale for using a QALY in clinical decision-making fails as a framework. ICER's continued use of the QALY in both the Value Framework and in its modified Framework for medicines that treat ultra-rare diseases will undermine the goals of personalized medicine."[90]

ICER Thresholds Are Arbitrary

The complexity, diversity, and severity of orphan and rare diseases present many complex ethical, contextual, and treatment challenges. ICER's QALY thresholds are arbitrary enough when applied to traditional medicines, but when applied to treatments for rare diseases, they take on an additional—and even more troubling—arbitrariness.

On what authority does ICER claim that only therapies achieving a QALY of less than $50,000 are "high value" therapies? The number may relate to a World Health Organization standard, but that standard itself is arbitrary. The thresholds are not scientific in any economic sense but rather, in placing a specific value on a human life, are a kind of theological dogma that must be accepted on faith as an objective standard. Yet, the entire superstructure of QALY methodology is built on these arbitrary dogmas which, if questioned, render the entire model illegitimate.

The arbitrariness of QALY thresholds has particularly troubling consequences when used to recommend that rare disease drugs do not deserve coverage unless their prices can be compressed to fit the assumptions of the model. As the *Journal of Comparative Effectiveness Research* study concludes: "QALYs, conceptualized as a preference-based measure of individual health-related outcomes combining quality and length of life, seemingly fail to capture the full social value of URD technologies;

hence their need to be complemented or replaced with alternatives that include societal preferences, such as concerns for equity in treatment." Without significant changes, "their application may lead to positively unethical conclusions that might deprive patients with URDs any chance of effective care."

ICER's Definition of "Ultra-Rare Disease" Is Also Arbitrary

When ICER drafted its revised framework for assessing the value of rare disease drugs, the patient advocacy community expressed disappointment at what it saw as ICER's arbitrary restriction of the proposed framework to diseases with 10,000 patients or less. Such a patient population cohort size corresponds to no definitions of rare or ultra-rare diseases under any U.S. legal or regulatory framework. ICER justified the figure by pointing out that it was "modestly higher than the threshold used in the EU."[91]

Pointing to one arbitrary threshold to justify another did not satisfy patient advocates. After all, many treatments for rare and devastating diseases would not, it was thought, benefit from the more generous thresholds that the new framework might provide. For example, patients with two relatively rare and serious diseases, sickle cell disease and hemophilia, may soon benefit from gene therapies to treat those diseases, yet neither disease will likely be considered ultra-rare by ICER.

The National Organization for Rare Disorders (NORD) issued a blistering comment about ICER's restriction of its revised framework to diseases with 10,000 patients or fewer.[92] Pointing to ICER's claim that a revised methodology should only be used for these smaller populations, NORD wrote, "We find this claim to be baseless and unfounded, and the lack of any outside citation or justification only furthers our conviction. There are many factors that contribute to the difficulty of evidence generation for orphan therapies, and we are confident that they do not start or stop at the 10,000 prevalence number. For example, many diseases with prevalence above 10,000 are even more difficult to develop therapies for due to the heterogeneity of the manifestation, progression, and severity of the diseases, as well as the variability

of treatments." Thus, given the arbitrary nature of ICER's definition of rare diseases, as well as the subjectiveness of its QALY
thresholds, we have to assume that both were chosen to cast the
widest possible net for the broader and more severe price control
regime that is at the heart of ICER's model.

Conclusion

In early 2017, when ICER announced it would make "modifications" to its "value framework" for ultra-rare disease treatments, it was essentially conceding that its model was failing to
capture the value society attaches to those therapies. In short,
ICER was saying that its model did not work for rare diseases.

At the time of the announcement, there was hope in the
patient advocacy community that ICER might show flexibility
when valuing many of the promising rare disease treatments. As
the new framework was developed, however, it became clear that
patient advocates' hopes were misplaced. Not only would it be
limited to very small populations, but the revised framework was
not substantially different from its predecessor.

ICER's continuing negative reviews of rare disease drugs
seem to indicate that its goal is not to accommodate the unique
contextual challenges of rare disease therapies, but simply to
push prices down without really considering the value that treatments bring to patients. Moreover, an argument can be made
that ICER increasingly sees its mission as scrutinizing orphan
disease drugs. Its rush to issue a negative value assessment of
Zolgensma on the very day the drug was approved by the FDA
seems to reflect ICER's inordinate focus on discounting the value
of rare disease treatments.

In early 2019, ICER announced yet another project to revise
its methodology for rating "potentially curative treatments" such
as "gene therapies."[93] This ongoing project is a further acknowl-
edgment that ICER's model is ill-suited to assessing cutting-edge
treatments emerging from biopharmaceutical laboratories.

ICER's constant rethinking of its model should give pause
about its "top down" approach to assessing the value of drug
therapies. Just maybe a "bottom up" approach in which patients,

their physicians, their caregivers, their health plan, and a variety of social actors make judgements about the value of particular therapies for particular patients would be a more flexible and, thus, more equitable approach, maybe not one favored by those economists who want to control healthcare decisions made by others, but certainly one most Americans would likely favor.

ICER's approach to rare disease drugs is highly troubling for patients with these diseases, for the physicians who treat them, and for the loved ones who care for them. Never has the prospect of breakthrough cures for some of the most terrible diseases that plague humankind been greater. Our knowledge of human chemistry, biology, and genetics is increasing exponentially, and that knowledge is beginning to bear fruit in the form of drug approvals.

Why, at this moment in history, would policy makers and payers consciously choose to adopt a cost-effectiveness model that is not only arbitrary, but is particularly ill-suited to evaluate the very therapies that will be born from our explosion in knowledge? A short time after Zolgensma was approved, Acting FDA Commissioner Ned Sharpless was asked in an interview about the costs of gene therapies. Even though the costs of medications are not in the FDA's jurisdiction,

Sharpless nonetheless expressed frustration at the focus of the question when the scientific progress for patients was so stunning. Of Zolgensma, Sharpless said, "This is a completely novel, almost magical miracle that ends a devastating disease for lots of little kids and the thing you care the most about is the price? I mean, really? If you are so cynical you can't see how wonderful and great this is…you need to rewear your happy hat."[94] Indeed.

CHAPTER 6

Other Questions for Legislators about the Institute of Clinical and Economic Review

Throughout this book, I have tried to present the risks that ICER's use of QALY potentially poses for different patient populations. In an evaluation framework that relies on QALY, as ICER's does, older patients, cancer patients, those with disabilities, and those suffering from rare diseases all potentially face restriction in access to potentially life-saving and life-extending treatments. I now turn my attention to other questions that legislators should ask as they consider adopting ICER's QALY method at either the state or federal level.

Questions about the Potential Limitations of ICER's Model

In 2016, the *Journal of Stem Cell Research & Therapy* conducted a literature review of the limitations of the application of the Quality Adjusted Life Year methodology to cost-effectiveness reviews; as discussed, QALY is the core measuring stick of ICER's model. The article argued that the academic literature displayed three general categories of limitations in the use of QALY:

1. Ethical Considerations
2. Methodological Issues and Theoretical Assumptions
3. Contextual or Condition-Specific Considerations

These three categories seem a useful way to organize questions that legislators or policy makers should ask about ICER's model. First, is it ethical? Does the model discriminate against certain therapies needed by vulnerable patients? And do those restrictions cross an ethical line beyond mere fiscal prudence into an ethically dubious realm that might be described as rationing and antilife?

Second, does the methodology used by ICER involve flawed "measurement techniques, tools, assumptions and mathematical operations" that call into question the validity of the model?

Finally, ICER effectively uses the same model to analyze most therapeutic areas. Is it a reliable guide to assessing the value of different therapies across these disease categories? It is widely recognized that the challenges, circumstances, genetic variations, and quality of life issues vary greatly among different disease states. It must be asked, then, whether a single model can capture and analyze this complexity and apply it compassionately to a variety of patient circumstances.

Ethical Considerations

Since the Hippocratic Oath of the fifth century BC, the provision of medical care has been commonly deemed to have a clear ethical dimension in which certain standards must be upheld. Without making judgments about the ethical validity of ICER's model, it is certainly conceivable that a cost-effectiveness framework that undervalued human life could represent an ethically dubious approach to medical care. The following are questions from the academic literature that may assist legislators in forming an opinion on the ethical component of ICER:

1. **Is it ethical to deny patients a new therapy pending an ICER review?**
   Comment: The political controversy in the UK surrounding oncology drugs was related to the National Health Service's unwillingness to provide a new renal cancer drug until the NICE review was complete. Some observers believe it would

be unethical to deny a treatment, particularly a life-saving or life-altering treatment, pending a cost-effectiveness review.

2. **Do QALY-based reviews capture the real-world experiences of patients with particular therapies?**
   Comment: Reviews based on QALY standards do not generally capture patient reporting on their experiences with particular medications. While ICER does "consult" with patient advocates, patient data is not incorporated into its reviews. Patient reporting, which is seen as increasingly important for physicians, the FDA, and health plans, seems a valuable data point that is omitted in most ICER reviews.

3. **Is the use of ICER reviews simply a method of dodging political accountability for rationing medicine?**
   Comment: As described in the book's introduction, in 1995, UK Minister of Health Gerry Malone was asked to decide whether the National Health Service should pay for Beta-interferon for multiple sclerosis. He made a compromise decision to cover the drug in certain cases. But he later told his staff that he never wanted to be faced with such decisions and they needed to develop an alternative mechanism to make them. Malone told his staff: "This is not something that in my view should ever again land on a minister's desk." Malone's desire to avoid accountability for difficult decisions led to the creation of NICE. It might be asked if relying solely on ICER's reviews is simply a device used by governments and politicians to avoid responsibility, and provide political cover for denying drugs to patients under the guise of an "independent review"?

4. **Wouldn't the use of ICER reviews drive profitability for private sector health plans and pharmacy benefit managers (PBMs), and represent a conflict of interest?**
   Comment: I would argue that the longevity and quality of life thresholds for ICER's QALY framework are set low in order

to generate reviews that conclude many specialty and rare disease drugs are not cost effective. To the degree that this provides health plans and their drug consultants, PBMs, with the political cover to deny these treatments to patients, ICER's review will drive up their profitability.

5. **Doesn't the QALY standard simply place an arbitrary value upon human life?**

   Comment: While it is an accepted practice among some economists to assign a monetary value to human life, the ethical implications of such a technique when it comes to actual medical care may be perilous. This raises an entire set of questions that might better be settled by religious leaders, ethicists, and physicians, among them: Is the monetary value of a small child or young mother the same as an older and frail patient? And who is best suited to be making these value judgments? Is it really an economist?

6. **Does the ICER review process interfere with autonomous physician-patient relationships?**

   Comment: Physicians and patients currently make drug therapy decisions based not simply on the efficacy of the drug options, but also on potential costs to the patient. An ICER review that precludes the availability of an expensive drug takes the decision out of the hands of the physician and patient.

7. **Is employing ICER's model a form of generational discrimination?**

   Comment: The effect of negative ICER reviews in certain therapeutic classes will undoubtedly diminish the interest of biopharmaceutical companies in conducting research in those classes. Therefore, can we not say that young patients, and patients yet to be born, who will contract these particular diseases are less likely to have a cure in the future.

Methodological Issues and Theoretical Assumptions

8. Is the use of meta-analysis, i.e. the pooling of results from different studies with different assumptions and analyzing different targets, often using different methodologies, a sound way to reach conclusions about specific drug therapies?

    Comment: Some ICER critics have argued that metadata analysis can be an unsound method for reaching accurate conclusions about specific drugs when the diverse metadata studies are combined into a single analysis.

9. Are ICER reviews conducted with adequate data?

    Comment: Typically, ICER conducts reviews shortly after, or even before, a therapy is approved by the FDA. Such a short time frame limits the review's ability to gauge the efficacy of a therapy in a larger number of patients or over longer intervals. Often, health plans reach valuable conclusions about the safety and efficacy of a medicine after it has been used by many thousands of patients over a long period of time. This larger and longer perspective may call into question the reliability of an earlier ICER review.

10. Does QALY analysis lead to inefficiencies in spending in the healthcare system?

    Comment: Some economists would argue that because QALYs establish arbitrary limits on drug spending, resources get diverted to other less deserving components of the healthcare system, creating inefficiencies.

11. Does QALY help legislators address budget challenges and shortfalls?

    Comment: QALY is intended to be an independent evaluation of therapies based on their value under the QALY assignment of monetary value to a therapy. That determination is wholly unrelated to the size of budgetary challenges of an individual state or payer.

12. **Is ICER methodology overly quantitative, and does it therefore fail to capture the variety of diverse circumstances that medical care presents?**
Comment: The delivery of medical care is a highly complex undertaking informed by a variety of factors related to age, gender, mental health, cost, et al. Attempting to capture all these factors in a single quantitative model may be problematic.

13. **Should quality of life measurements be determined by patients or the general population?**
Comment: QALY reviews generally determine quality-of-life improvement by consulting with the general population. Some patient advocates have argued that, for example, *improvements* in quality of life for oncology treatments should be measured by consulting with cancer patients who are more acutely aware of the value of treatments. Shouldn't ICER collect data from both the general public and specific patient populations when conducting its reviews? One study seems to indicate that patient input is not adequately represented in ICER reviews.

14. **Should ICER's methodology be transparent?**
Comment: Not all aspects of ICER's model are publicly available. Some observers believe that ICER, when conducting reviews for public programs, should be completely transparent so its model can be evaluated in the public square.

15. **How often should ICER reviews be updated?**
Comment: Some health policy experts argue that isolated reviews of a single drug therapy can become obsolete over time. Improvements in one drug therapy may improve the effectiveness of another therapy, making standards of care

an ever-evolving target. For example, improvements in the treatment of diabetes may improve the effectiveness of treatments for heart failure. How will ICER capture these evolutions in the standard of care?

16. **Is the use of list prices in ICER reviews a serious methodological flaw?**
Comment: There has been exponential growth in the size of rebates, discounts, and other fees paid to health plans and PBMs by drug manufacturers. By failing to capture these discounts, ICER's methodology doesn't accurately capture drug prices, and ICER cost-effectiveness reviews can involve errors of 30 percent or more for specific drugs, depending upon rebate levels.

17. **How long will ICER reviews take and will new drugs be available to patients pending the reviews?**
Comment: In the UK, NICE reviews for oncology drugs took so long that Parliament circumvented the NICE process and established a fund for cancer treatments that ignored NICE reviews. Patient advocates are concerned that ICER reviews will exhibit similar limitations in the US.

18. **Is it arbitrary to establish a global budget for drug spending?**
Comment: ICER's model caps annual drug spending. Ignoring the ebb and flow of biopharmaceutical pipelines may result in arbitrarily denying patients new treatments in a year when the pipeline is particularly robust.

19. **Does the use of QALY fail to capture the non-health benefits of drug therapies?**
Comment: As briefly discussed in Chapter 4, restoring a patient to good health can bring a variety of economic benefits not captured in ICER's model, such as economic productivity, return to caregiver status, better performance in school,

et al. ICER's model fails to adequately capture these types of economic benefits.

20. **Do QALYs discount the opinion of physicians in patient care?**

Comment: The decision to prescribe a particular drug to a particular patient cannot be made on the basis of a metadata study, as only a patient's physician can understand the complexity of the individual patient's circumstances.

21. **Does ICER's model discourage innovation?**

Comment: The US legal and regulatory regime for medicines encourages innovations in drug therapies that tend to make them expensive when they are patent-protected but inexpensive when the patents lapse. Because ICER only evaluates therapies based on the patent-protected price, its model fails to capture the societal benefits of new medicines once they become far less expensive.

Contextual or Condition-Specific Considerations

22. **Does ICER's model discriminate against preventive medicine?**

Comment: As I've discussed, ICER's model assigns value on two scales: longevity and improvements in quality of life. The value of medications that prevent disease do not seem to be adequately captured by this model.

23. **Will personalized medicine make ICER's model obsolete?**

Comment: As I touched on in my discussion in Chapter 5 of the potential impact of QALY on therapies for rare diseases, medical care is moving away from the "one-size-fits-all" model and toward precision medicine based on breakthroughs in genetics. Through diagnostic testing, physicians in the future will know which patients will respond to a certain therapy and which will not. ICER reviews may fail to adequately capture efficacy and variations in side effects based on a patient's genetic profile.

24. **Can ICER's model adequately capture the value of mental health treatments?**

As I noted in my discussion in Chapter 3 of the intersection of ICER's model with the ADA, of all disease categories, mental health is the most difficult therapeutic area in which to capture the value of various treatments to individual patients. Some data suggest that general public opinion, which ICER uses to weight quality of life (HRQoL) measures, underestimates the impact of mental health conditions compared with the opinion of patients.

25. **Does the use of QALYs fail to capture the value of important nuances within specific disease areas?**

Comment: For the treatment of rheumatoid arthritis, for example, a patient's quality of life — not longevity — is the only meaningful measure of value. For cancer patients, longevity tends to be the most important value. ICER uses the same model regardless of potential differences in patient values across disease areas.

Conclusion

Trends in biopharmaceutical research have pushed reimbursement for very expensive medications to the forefront in public policy debates. Policy makers must make difficult choices, balancing costs against patient access to new treatments.

ICER provides policy makers with one potential methodology — some would say a flawed methodology — to evaluate the cost-effectiveness of treatments using a set of assumptions that have significant limitations. Because of these limitations, which include my questions above about ICER's methodology and process, I cannot recommend policy makers rely on ICER reviews for their Medicaid and other state programs.

Whether a treatment is included in a formulary is a life and death decision. I cannot recommend adoption of a tool that raises so many ethical, methodological, and disease-specific questions. The British experience with cancer care should be a warning for legislators to probe deeply the implications of ICER's model for older Americans, the disabled, cancer patients, and those with rare diseases. Until these issues are fully addressed, ICER's model should be avoided.

Where do we go from here?

The Quality Adjusted Life Year (QALY) methodology has generally not met with a receptive audience in the American polity. While some payers are certainly interested in QALY so as to justify restricting access to certain therapies and, in that way, improve their bottom line, American politicians across the political spectrum have expressed serious reservations about QALY. There is some likelihood that the new Congress will restrict the use of QALY in federal programs.

On the left side of the spectrum, for example, politicians have expressed concerns about the impact of QALY on access to medicines for people living with disabilities and for people with chronic conditions. Maybe the most articulate advocate opposing QALY on the left side of the political spectrum is former House Democratic Whip, and disability rights advocate, Tony Coehlo. Coehlo, importantly, was one of the primary congressional authors of the Americans with Disabilities Act (ADA).

The Biden Administration has also weighed in on the QALY issue. On September 9, 2021, U.S. Health and Human Services Secretary Xavier Becerra released a report on Medicare drug prices in which he warned against the use of QALY in making decisions about access to therapies available in Medicare. He wrote, "There are important concerns about the equity implications of certain methodologies, such as Quality Adjusted Life Years (QALYs), for people of all ages with disabilities and chronic conditions. Drug pricing reforms should avoid utilization of methodologies that adversely impact access to needed medications for vulnerable populations."

On the right side of the political spectrum, there are also concerns about the use of QALY.

Similar to the concerns articulated by Democrats and Biden Administration officials, the Republican and conservative critique of QALY is likewise related to concerns about access, but for them there is greater emphasis on the danger of healthcare rationing within a "socialist" healthcare system that employs QALY. On April 28, 2022, three influential conservative GOP House members — Cathy McMorris Rodgers, Jim Banks, and Brad Wenstrup — introduced "The Protecting Health Care for All Patients Act." This legislation would ban the use of QALY by all federal programs providing drug therapies to patients. While these conservative legislators label their legislation as "pro-life," they also express a similar concern to those on the left — that QALY will threaten access to therapies for vulnerable populations such as citizens living with disabilities.

The widespread adoption of QALY would represent a philosophical sea change in American healthcare. Americans have historically supported a healthcare system that is more expensive than other nations in return for higher quality and better access. While much is made of price disparities for prescription drugs between the U.S. and other developed nations, it is less well understood that costs of physician services and hospital procedures are also significantly higher in the U.S. As a general matter, Americans have not been willing to accept second-rate healthcare or to tolerate long waits for access to first-rate healthcare.

And in return for higher costs, Americans do indeed receive a higher quality of care and with far shorter wait times. Regarding prescription drugs, for example, Americans receive access to 87% of newly approved medicines within three months of their approval. Canadians, by contrast, only receive access to 46% of new medicines and wait 15 months for that access.[95]

Congress recently enacted pharmaceutical price controls on a limited number of Medicare drugs. This was viewed as a political victory for the President and congressional Democrats. If the Inflation Reduction Act does succeed in reducing patient out-of-pocket costs for commonly prescribed drugs, it will be viewed favorably by many Americans. If, however, the law results in Medicare denials of prescription drugs to Medicare patients — an outcome that is a distinct possibility — the law may be viewed far less favorably. Americans will not be happy if they are denied a prescription drug recommended by their physician.

In this context, a ban on the use of QALY would likely be a political winner for both Republicans and Democrats, as the entire purpose of QALY is to invent an "objective" justification to deny patients a new therapy. Banning QALY would prevent its use in denying Americans access to the latest therapies. This would not only be popular, it would, much more importantly, help ensure patients have access to drugs that might save their lives.

ENDNOTES

1 https://www.forbes.com/sites/theapothecary/2017/09/30/the-3-reason-bernie-sanders-medicare-for-all-single-payer-plan-is-a-singularly-bad-idea/?sh=2a414a6c3a70

2 https://www.cdc.gov/coronavirus/2019-ncov/specific-groups/high-risk-complications.html

3 https://jme.bmj.com/content/31/12/685.full

4 https://ora.ox.ac.uk/objects/uuid:d22a9b1b-c2f0-4f6c-83ee-fdc320e4af61/download_file?file_format=pdf&safe_filename=The%2Blimitations%2Bof%2BQALY%253B%2Ba%2Bliterature%2Breview.pdf&type_of_work=Journal+article

5 https://jme.bmj.com/content/38/5/258

6 https://icer.org/wp-content/uploads/2018/12/QALY_evLYG_12122018.pdf

7 https://cevr.tuftsmedicalcenter.org/news/2018/will-icers-response-to-attacks-on-the-qaly-quiet-the-critics

8 https://www.npr.org/templates/story/story.php?storyId=121283688

9 https://www.ncbi.nlm.nih.gov/pubmed/16435466

10 https://www.nber.org/papers/w11405

11 https://icer-review.org/announcements/icer-describes-qaly/

12 At this time, it cannot be said with certainty that the quality-of-life methodology, used most prominently by the Institute for Clinical and Economic Review ("ICER") for rating the cost-effectiveness of medical treatments and therapies, violates or complies with the Americans with Disabilities Act ("ADA"). There has yet to be a decision issued by the Supreme Court that would govern such a case. In addition, no cases currently pending before the Supreme Court from the previous term or the upcoming term will address the issue.

13 42 U.S.C. § 12131(2).

14 42 U.S.C. §§ 1396 – 1396w-5; *Hines v. Shalala*, 999 F.2d 684, 686 (2d. Cir. 1993).

15 *See Hines*, 999 F.2d at 686 citing *New York v. Sullivan*, 894 F.2d 20, 21-22 (2d. Cir. 1990).

16 42 U.S.C. §§ 12101(a)(1), (2), (3), (5).

17 42 U.S.C. § 12131(1).

18 42 U.S.C. § 12132.

19 42 U.S.C. § 12132; *Fulton v. Goord,* 591 F.3d 37, 43 (2d.Cir. 2009).

20 *See Taylor v. Colorado Dept. of Health Care Policy and Financing,* 811 F.3d 1230, 1233-35 (3d Cir. 2016); *Cohon ex rel. Bass v. New Mexico Dept. of Health,* 646 F.3d 717, 724-25 (10th Cir. 2011); *Arc of California v. Douglas,* 956 F. Supp.2d 1113, 1121-22 (E.D. Cal. 2013), *rev'd in part* 757 F.3d 975.

21 *Dean v. Univ. at Buffalo Sch. of Med.,* 804 F.3d 178, 189 (2d. Cir. 2015).

22 *Gamble v. City of Escondido*, 104 F.3d 300, 306 (9th Cir. 1997).

23 *See* 28 C.F.R. § 35.130(d).

24 *Olmstead v. L.C. ex rel. Zimring,* 527 U.S. 581 (1999).

25 *See Davis v. Shah*, 821 F.3d 231, 260 (2d. Cir. 2016).

26 *Amundson ex rel. Amundson v. Wisconsin Dept. of Health Servs.,* 721 F.3d 871, 874 (7th Cir. 2013), citing *Olmstead,* 527 U.S. at 597-603.

27 *Helen L.,* 46 F.3d at 331-33; *Soto v. City of Newark,* 72 F. Supp.2d 489, 493 (D.N.J. 1999); *Darian v. Univ. of Mass. Bos.,* 980 F. Supp. 77, 89 (D. Mass. 1997); *Niece v. Fitzner,* 922 F. Supp. 1208, 1217 (E.D. Mich. 1996); *Lincoln CERCPAC v. Health and Hosps. Corp.,* 920 F. Supp. 488, 497 (S.D.N.Y. 1996)

28 28 C.F.R. § 35.130.

29 https://www.cdc.gov/nchs/fastats/leading-causes-of-death.htm

30 https://www.iqvia.com/insights/the-iqvia-institute/reports/medicine-spending-and-affordability-in-the-us

31 https://www.thelancet.com/journals/eclinm/article/PIIS2589-5370(20)30369-2/fulltext

32 https://www.biospace.com/article/biden-harris-unveil-prescription-drug-pricing-plans/

33 https://www.idsihealth.org/wp-content/uploads/2016/02/A-TERRIBLE-BEAUTY_resize.pdf

34 https://www.idsihealth.org/wp-content/uploads/2016/02/A-TERRIBLE-BEAUTY_resize.pdf

35 https://www.idsihealth.org/wp-content/uploads/2016/02/A-TERRIBLE-BEAUTY_resize.pdf

36 https://ascopost.com/issues/september-25-2018/care-for-the-cancer-caregiver/

37 https://www.geriatric.theclinics.com/article/S0749-0690(04)00064-3/fulltext

38 https://journals.lww.com cancernursingonline/pages/articleviewer.aspx?year=2015&issue=07000&article=00013&type=abstract

39 https://journals.lww.com/cancernursingonline/pages/article viewer.aspx?year=2015&issue=07000&article=00013&type=abstract

40 https://cevr.tuftsmedicalcenter.org/news/2020/societal-perspective

41 https://www.jmcp.org/doi/pdf/10.18553/jmcp.2020.26.5.652

42 https://sgp.fas.org/crs/misc/R45792.pdf

43 https://www.ncbi.nlm.nih.gov/pmc/articles/PMC5692723/

44 https://www.sciencedirect.com/science/article/pii/S2213538316300236

45 https://www.nmqf.org/nmqf-media/traditional-value-assessment-methods

46 https://www.sciencedirect.com/science/article/pii/S2213538316300236

47 https://www.sciencedirect.com/science/article/pii/S2213538316300236

48 https://pubmed.ncbi.nlm.nih.gov/21599035/

49 https://pubmed.ncbi.nlm.nih.gov/21599035/

50 https://www.cancer.net/navigating-cancer-care/how-cancer-treated/personalized-and-targeted-therapies/what-personalized-cancer-medicine

51 https://www.personalizedmedicinecoalition.org/Userfiles/PMC-Corporate/file/PMC_on_ICER_2020_Proposed_Updates.pdf

52 https://www.personalizedmedicinecoalition.org/Userfiles/PMC-Corporate/file/PMC_on_ICER_2020_Proposed_Updates.pdf

53 https://www.hmpgloballearningnetwork.com/site/jcp/article/personalized-medicine-world-value-frameworks

54 https://personalizedmedicine.blog/2016/06/29/icer-personalized-medicine-time-to-engage/

55 https://icer.org/assessment/multiple-myeloma-2021/

56 https://www.myeloma.org/blog/dr-duries/icer-blinks-patients-benefit

57 https://www.healio.com/news/hematology-oncology/20160928/icer-report-questions-value-of-myeloma-regimens-but-critics-say-findings-dont-translate-to-practice

58 https://www.obroncology.com/article/op-ed-our-view-on-value-frameworks-in-oncology-proposing-principles-for-value-framework-development

59 https://www.cancer.gov/publications/dictionaries/cancer-terms/def/progression-free-survival

60 https://www.myeloma.org/blog/dr-duries/icer-blinks-patients-benefit

61 https://www.walshmedicalmedia.com/open-access/the-limitations-of-qaly-a-literature-review-2157-7633-1000334.pdf

62 https://www.thelancet.com/journals/eclinm/article/PIIS2589-5370(20)30369-2/fulltext

63 https://www.cancer.gov/about-cancer/understanding/statistics

64 https://old-prod.asco.org/about-asco/press-center/news-releases/national-cancer-opinion-survey-2020-new-findings

65 https://jamanetwork.com/journals/jamaoncology/article-abstract/2532353?resultClick=1

66 https://drugstorenews.com/iqvia-report-global-medicine-spending-top-11t-2024

67 https://www.bbc.com/news/health-11630699

68 https://www.managedcaremag.com/archives/2018/12/cvs-and-100000-qaly

69 https://www.walshmedicalmedia.com/open-access/the-limitations-of-qaly-a-literature-review-2157-7633-1000334.pdf

70 https://www.fda.gov/industry/medical-products-rare-diseases-and-conditions

71 https://www.iqvia.com/form-pages/institute-gated?redirect Url=%2f-%2fmedia%2fiqvia%2fpdfs%2finstitute-reports%2for phan-drugs-in-the-united-states-growth-trends-in-rare -disease-treatments.pdf%3f_%3d1553789128318&Name= Orphan+Drugs+in+the+United+States+Growth+Trends+ in+Rare+Disease+Treatments

72 https://www.rheumatology.org/Learning-Center/Statistics

73 https://www.cdc.gov/cholesterol/facts.htm

74 https://www.iqvia.com/insights/the-iqvia-institute/reports/ medicine-use-and-spending-in-the-us-review-of-2017-outlook-to-2022

75 https://www.iqvia.com/insights/the-iqvia-institute/reports/ the-global-use-of-medicine-in-2019-and-outlook-to-2023

76 https://www.iqvia.com/form-pages/institute-gated?redirec tUrl=%2f-%2fmedia%2fiqvia%2fpdfs%2finstitute-reports%2fo rphan-drugs-in-the-united-states-growth-trends-in-rare-diseas e-treatments.pdf%3f_%3d1553789128318&Name=Orphan+ Drugs+in+the+United+States+Growth+Trends+in+Rare+ Disease+Treatments

77 https://www.iqvia.com/insights/the-iqvia-institute/reports/ the-global-use-of-medicine-in-2019-and-outlook-to-2023

78 https://www.iqvia.com/insights/the-iqvia-institute/reports/ medicine-use-and-spending-in-the-us-review-of-2017-outlook-to-2022

79 https://icer.org/news-insights/press-releases/proposed-vaf-changes-ultra-rare/

80 https://academic.oup.com/bmb/article/96/1/5/300011

81 https://blog.panalgo.com/blog

82 https://pioneerinstitute.org/featured/study-urges-caution-before-adopting-icer-reviews-to-determine-cost-effectiveness-of-treatments/

83 https://www.futuremedicine.com/doi/full/10.2217/cer.14.34

84 https://www.healthaffairs.org/do/10.1377/hblog20181105.38350/ full/

85 https://icer.org/wp-content/uploads/2018/07/ICER_SMA_Final_ Evidence_Report_052419.pdf

86 https://www.futuremedicine.com/doi/full/10.2217/cer.14.34

87 https://icer.org/wp-content/uploads/2018/07/ICER_SMA_Final_
Evidence_Report_052419.pdf

88 https://icer.org/wp-content/uploads/2018/07/ICER_SMA_Final_
Evidence_Report_052419.pdf

89 https://www.walshmedicalmedia.com/open-access/the-
limitations-of-qaly-a-literature-review-2157-7633-1000334.pdf

90 https://www.bio.org/sites/default/files/legacy/bioorg/docs/
BIO%20Final%20Comments_ICER%20Rare%20Disease%20
Revisions_9-25-17.pdf

91 https://icer.org/wp-content/uploads/2017/11/ICER-Adaptations-
of-Value-Framework-for-Rare-Diseases.pdf

92 https://rarediseases.org/wp-content/uploads/2014/11/NORD-
Comments-on-Proposed-Adaptation-of-the-ICER-Value-
Frameowrk-for-the-Assessment-of-Treatments-for-Ultra-Rare-
Conditions.docx.pdf

93 https://icer.org/announcements/icer-launches-international-
collaborative-to-develop-new-meth-ods-to-guide-value-based-
pricing-of-potential-cures/

94 https://endpts.com/ned-sharpless-weighs-in-on-gene-therapy-
pricing-debate-suggesting-the-messaging-got-lost/

95 https://www.phrma.org/medicare/the-united-states-vs-other-
countries-availability-of-new-medicines-varies